CREATION? Really?

A CONVERSATION ON ORIGINS

LEONARD BRAND

Pacific Press®
Publishing Association
Nampa, Idaho | www.pacificpress.com

Cover design by Gerald Lee Monks
Cover design resources
   Car: iStockphoto | AnjaRabenstein;
   Desert: iStockphoto | binkski

Published by Pacific Press® Publishing Association
Printed in the United States of America.

The author assumes full responsibility for the accuracy of all facts and quotations as cited in this book.

Additional copies of this book may be purchased by calling toll-free 1-800-765-6955 or by visiting AdventistBookCenter.com.

ISBN 978-0-8163-6502-9

February 2019

Dedication

Dedicated to Ariel Roth, who started me on a path toward understanding science, its strengths and boundaries, and the relationship between science and Scripture, and acquainted me and so many others with the geological record in western North America. I will never forget those demanding and fascinating field excursions or Ariel's creative tomato–rice soup sandwiches.

Also by Leonard Brand

Beginnings (2005)

The Prophet and Her Critics (2005)

Choose You This Day (2013)

Contents

Preface

The controversy over how the earth and its life-forms began has been going on for centuries, and it continues. It has become even more animated and intense in this era. The question is still debated: Did God create, as the book of Genesis describes, or did the earth and life just happen?

In this book of conversation, Carl, a creationist, and Ed, an evolutionist, find that they are on opposite sides of the issue, and their discussion leads into questions that we all face, even though we may not think about them often. Their views represent two of the prominent conceptual frameworks that we use to relate faith and science. As this debate proceeds, I hope you will gain a growing understanding of the issues that underlie the evidence and how we interpret that evidence.

Of course, this is not a record of a real-life conversation. It is my attempt to re-create what could very well be a real conversation, based on what I hear and read of things that creation-oriented scientists and conventional scientists say about each other, as well as some personal conversations I have been involved in. I attempt to convey as accurately as I can how these two groups view each other and how their understanding of the evidence and its interpretation is best portrayed. It is not meant to be a completely comprehensive treatment of the two views, but rather I chose to include especially significant factors affecting how the two groups interpret earth and biological history.

In the end, each of us must make our own choice. We need to be informed enough to make an educated choice.

The original manuscript was reviewed and improved by Ariel Roth, Art Chadwick, Kurt Wise, Kim Brand, Ronny Nalin, Dennis Brand,

Cedric Clendenon, Trent Logan, Fernando Dávila Garriga, Matt Mc-Lain, Birgir Oskarsson, and Paul Giem. Of course, I own any remaining problems.

Leonard Brand
June 16, 2018

The geological record, with some typical fossils to illustrated differences in the fossils around in different parts of the fossil record. Dates in millions of years, as understood in the standard geological timescale. Modified from Brand and Chadwick, 2016, *Faith, Reason and Earth History*.

ERA	PERIOD	EPOCH	EVENTS	TYPICAL FOSSILS
CENOZOIC	Quaternary	Holocene Pleistocene		
CENOZOIC	Tertiary	Pliocene		
CENOZOIC	Tertiary	Miocene		
CENOZOIC	Tertiary	Oligocene		
CENOZOIC	Tertiary	Eocene		
CENOZOIC	Tertiary	Paleocene		
		66 my	Abundant coal Rocky Mts	
MESOZOIC	Cretaceous			
MESOZOIC	Jurassic			
MESOZOIC	Triassic			
		252 my		
PALEOZOIC	Permian			
PALEOZOIC	Pennsylvanian		Abundant coal Appalachian Mts	
PALEOZOIC	Mississippian			
PALEOZOIC	Devonian			
PALEOZOIC	Silurian			
PALEOZOIC	Ordovician			
PALEOZOIC	Cambrian			
		541 my	Cambrian explosion	
PRECAMBRIAN				

CHAPTER 1

Controversy

The following conversation is between Carl, who believes in God and a literal Creation, and Ed, who doesn't believe in either. They are going on a geology field trip together in the western United States, and their differing views dominate the conversations during the trip. If you are not familiar with scientific or biblical terms or concepts in the following chapters, you may wish to spend some time in the glossary on page 93 and the figure on page 9.

CARL. There, I think we're ready to go. We have our rock hammers, field notebooks, GPS, topographic maps, a jug of water, and plenty of lunch. You brought the shovel, which will be important if we get stuck in the sand. I'm glad you could come along, as it is a lot safer to have two of us together out in the wilderness. And I have the research permit that allows us to study the stone in the abandoned flagstone quarries. We have a long drive ahead of us.

ED. It's my pleasure to go with you. I look forward to being part of this research trip. But I'm curious about your approach to the research. We'll be studying the Coconino Sandstone at our first stop, which essentially all geologists believe was eolian, formed by the wind into desert sand dunes. You suggest it was not eolian but was deposited underwater, right? This should be an interesting trip!

CARL. It's true that I consider possible explanations that are not taken seriously by many other scientists. I want to know what explanation best fits the evidence, whether that explanation is popular or not. Are you comfortable with that?

ED. I will actually enjoy exploring some novel ideas. But do you worry that your approach could be influenced by your religious views? By your belief in the biblical Creation and literal Flood? I don't object to the Bible belief, but is it possible that it might bring some types of bias into the research? You may be aware that there is plenty of concern about that sort of thing among qualified scientists.

CARL. Oh, yes. Some geologists are afraid that people like me are trying to prove the global flood described in the Bible. And to be fair, some of them *are* trying to prove it. That is not my approach.

I read widely in the literature that argues that creationists are wrong and ignorant, so I am definitely aware of the concerns. I presume you have read Jerry Coyne's book *Faith Versus Fact*. He leaves no doubt what he thinks about it—faith has nothing to contribute to the discussion. In his view, a discussion between religion and science will be a monologue. Religious people would have nothing to say!

ED. You've certainly noticed that Jerry Coyne doesn't tiptoe around the issues. He doesn't think it's possible for religious people to accomplish viable science research. Others may use gentler words, but many still share his thinking. I am personally willing to work on keeping an open mind, but you will need to convince me. The scientific worries about religious bias in research have been growing for a couple hundred years, and that has become a solid part of, well, the scientific attitude.

CARL. We can address these concerns in the most practical way when we start looking at the rocks and trying to interpret them. For now, let me mention an example that I find useful in illustrating the bias problem. I presume you're familiar with biology textbooks and other books that discuss how the first living things arrived—transitioning from the nonliving world to the first living cells. All those books I have read describe in clear certainty that life arose by the naturalistic process of chemical evolution, or abiogenesis.

In these descriptions, life happened by natural processes—the laws of chemistry and physics—with absolutely no intelligent input. How much evidence supports this interpretation? Can physical evidence be presented to support this idea? Is there evidence that shows this to be the only valid, or even the most valid, explanation?

ED. You've presented a challenging example! Of course, you do realize that life began so long ago that finding evidence is almost impossible. So perhaps you are expecting too much.

CARL. I am expecting a lot, but this emphasizes my point. We have no direct evidence about the origin of the first life, so how can anyone have so much confidence that we know how life began? How can we test hypotheses for life's origins?

ED. You must be aware that biochemists do test such hypotheses. Researchers are studying the RNA world as possibly the first chemical stage in the origin of life, preceding proteins and DNA. RNA molecules can serve as catalysts for biochemical reactions, in addition to their role in genetics, which makes RNA an ideal molecule for beginning life. This is testing a life-origins hypothesis. Why does this not answer your skepticism?

CARL. I do agree with you, but only in part. You're describing some good laboratory science but not addressing the larger question. Biochemists are seeking to understand how chemical processes could occur *by chance* to result in a living cell. This has resulted in some good biochemistry research that may not have been done otherwise. This is, I suggest, an example of a bad hypothesis or theory leading to insightful research and biochemical advances. This is not uncommon in science. The scientific value of a hypothesis has more to do with its ability to stimulate productive research than with the ultimate truth of the hypothesis.

To understand what is happening here, however, we have to look at the larger context. If it is even possible for life to begin without a creator, it would have been a very long sequence of random, rambling biochemical events—millions of reactions, probably billions. But for this discussion we can be conservative and suggest it would take a million such events. The RNA world involves only a handful of these events and is seeking to determine if it was possible, perhaps, for RNA to fill the needed role for this very small segment of the million events. This has led to some fruitful biochemistry research, but it does not address the larger question: Did biochemistry—and not a designer or creator—bring life into existence? Does the evidence show that life arose by chemical evolution rather than by the work of an intelligent designer? It cannot answer that question. And the RNA-world research is not succeeding in its attempt to show that RNA can fill the proposed role in origins, even in a small segment of the million steps.

ED. OK, a valiant effort, and the problems you describe are real. We don't know how life began. But modern science can't deal with supernatural ideas—that is the big item that you've missed! It is simply not possible for science to test whether a god or some kind of designer was involved in the origin of anything. Science has made tremendous progress since abandoning supernatural explanations. I suspect you really do believe there is a god. But the idea of a God that can do supernatural miracles—how can we reconcile that with our modern understanding of the laws of chemistry and physics?

CARL. In time I will try to give some answers to those questions. For now, can we agree that the foundation of our understanding of the origin of life is dependent on something other than the evidence? That it's something to do with philosophy and assumptions? We could discuss, or even argue about, the biochemical evidence all day, and at the end we would still differ for reasons that are not based on the available evidence itself. Is that not true?

ED. I'm thinking about that—and I guess it's correct. We do agree on that much, but there's much more we need to talk about.

CARL. That's true, but if we're going to make it through this trip, maybe today we should discuss something less controversial. Maybe politics!

ED. Good idea!

CARL. While we've talked, the miles have slipped past. We're about to turn onto Interstate 40 at Barstow, California, the interstate's western-most point. Notice that sign over there?

ED. "Wilmington, North Carolina, 2,554 miles"! Somebody in the highway department has a sense of humor.

CARL. Absolutely! We won't be going that far, but our first stop will be in Arizona.

CHAPTER 2

Assumptions, Questions, and Science

After a rigorous discussion of politics, the two scientists are closer to their Arizona destination.

CARL. Since we've reached an agreement in our critique of current politics and decided that the Republicans and the Democrats are all of questionable virtue, we can move on to other topics.

Interstate 40 has served us well, carrying us quickly into Arizona. In the next town is the Roadkill Cafe, and despite its name, it has pretty good food. It's in Seligman, famous for its tourist emphasis on Highway 66 history. Shall we stop?

ED. We might as well. I haven't had any roadkill for a long time!

CARL. Soon we'll be turning off I-40, heading to the area with flagstone quarries. The flagstone, from Coconino Sandstone, is quarried and sold for building material. They don't actually build buildings from the flagstone, as they do with limestone, but the quarried sandstone slabs are used for decorating or for building walls along property lines. My interest is in learning how the sandstone was formed—in what ancient environment was the sand deposited?

ED. I'm curious why you suggest the sandstone was deposited underwater instead of in a desert, as everyone else thinks. Why are you being difficult? You mentioned that some geologists think you are trying to prove that old story of Noah's flood described in the Bible. Is there anything to that?

CARL. I can answer your question if you will answer another question first. There are many rock formations, and the sediment that forms many of them is generally believed to have been deposited by water. A few others are thought to have been deposited by wind. If we find that *one additional* formation, the Coconino Sandstone, was formed underwater, how would that prove Noah's catastrophic flood?

ED. Science doesn't properly claim to prove things. Only advertisements on TV prove things! Just kidding—they don't really prove anything, no matter what they are paid to say. Science finds evidence that can support or challenge a theory, and it is always possible that new evidence will refute what seemed to be a good theory. This is why science doesn't prove things.

To answer your question more directly, I guess changes in the explanation of one rock formation can't prove or disprove a grand-scale idea like the Bible's great flood. Is that what you mean?

CARL. Yes, I would never claim to have proved the Flood on evidence alone. And I liked your description of why science doesn't prove things. It tells us that science can't give us truth with certainty. As you say, new evidence can always disprove what seemed like a good theory. Consequently, we can't claim our scientific theories as truth. Science just shows us which are the best models or theories that we have, based on the evidence that is now available from the study of nature and, as always, subject to the assumptions science is using.

But I know why some might want to accuse Bible-believing researchers of trying to prove the Flood. People like me do think differently about the history of our earth, and that makes some other scientists nervous. Coming back to your original question, I became interested in the Coconino because of some papers I read that described fossilized animal trackways in the sandstone. It seemed to me the story of how this happened needed more study. I do think there was a great flood, and I wondered if this sandstone with its animal tracks was formed in that flood, or if the tracks were not formed in water.

ED. As you say, that does make me nervous. What do you mean when you say you think differently about the history of the earth?

CARL. Some of us believe that the geological record with its fossils developed in a more catastrophic, rapid manner.

ED. Aren't you letting your religion interfere with science?

CARL. It could interfere if I were to let it. This is an important point, and I will try to clearly explain. One step in research is asking a question. The next step is trying to answer it. A question can come from many different places, like from what we read or see in the rocks. Or—and this is the part you may disagree with—the question could even come from my biblical beliefs.

ED. Yes, you are losing me on that one. Like I said, religion is getting mixed up with science.

CARL. In a way it is, but whether that is a problem depends on what I do with the second step—answering the question. No matter where the *question* comes from, if I seek a scientific *answer* I must use the accepted scientific process to search for the answer; in this case, for the explanation of how those animal trackways formed. It will be necessary to make careful observations, to collect evidence—data— and use that evidence to answer the question.

If I do that, the question is getting a scientific answer, no matter where the question came from.

ED. So you propose that any question, even a crazy question, can lead to legitimate research if it can be answered with methods that any scientist can use?

CARL. Well, I would say any reasonable question can function that way. Ah—here we are—we have arrived at the quarry I was looking for. See the fossil trackways on the cross-bedded sandstones over there? The trackways go up these sloping sand surfaces. If I am asking whether the animals making the tracks were on a desert dune or an underwater sand wave, is that not fair? I suggest it is a more open-minded search than if I began with the unproven assumption that they formed in a desert and then considered only explanations allowed under that assumption.

ED. I can see your point, but I'm not used to thinking that way. The eolian desert interpretation is so well accepted, supported by a lot of evidence, that it doesn't seem realistic to doubt its accuracy.

CARL. Many geologists see it that way. But think back a few decades to the time before 1960, when it was quite uniformly agreed among geologists that the theory of continental drift was not valid. Then some new evidence came to light, and in a few years, continental drift and plate tectonics became uniformly accepted.

In, say, 1955, a scientist who was willing to take seriously the possibility of moving continents would have looked like a maverick, when in fact he or she was making the wise choice. Should we learn anything from that episode? We can't spend our time chasing every novel idea that anyone suggests, but if some evidence raises doubts about an accepted theory, it could be wise to not be too committed to the favored theory.

ED. Sure, that logic looks good, because we can look back and see that the unconventional maverick was on the right track. But it seems that we know the history of this Coconino Sandstone already. Why spend time chasing the wild idea, as you say, that the Coconino Sandstone was not a desert deposit? Don't these sandstone surfaces look like they were once part of a sand dune?

CARL. Before 1960, all of us geologists also thought the idea of drifting continents was clearly wrong. Why should we now think that we have all our other ideas "in the bag," with no possibility we are wrong again? There are evidence-based reasons for questioning the eolian interpretation of the Coconino, and science has had to make many of these changes of direction in our theories. I prefer to think for myself on some of these things.

I will also admit that I have a theological reason for my questioning, and this may make you nervous again. I would like to find evidence of whether the Coconino could have been, or could not have been, formed during a time when water covered this land. I am willing to ask questions that others may not think worth asking, and in my experience this willingness to ask new questions often results in significant insights that would be missed if we limited ourselves to the "conventional" questions that everyone else is asking.

I will make one other point on this issue, then I will be quiet. Remember our discussion of the origin of the first life-forms? I think we concluded that the accepted theory of biochemical evolution was based more on naturalistic assumptions than on evidence, and yet it is a firmly held belief of many scientists. I can't help wondering what other accepted theories are in the same category—widely and firmly accepted and yet based on assumption rather than evidence?

ED. Since you have given me the last word on this topic, I will say that you make some good points, but still this does leave me a little nervous, so you will need to convince me that you are not abusing the scientific process.

CARL. OK, let's leave the philosophizing and look more carefully at these rocks. Maybe that will help.

CHAPTER 3

Puzzles in Sandstone

CARL. This flagstone quarry is one that I have studied before. We'll park here, and we'll have plenty of sandstone to look at.

ED. This is a beautiful example of cross-bedded sandstone, with sets of sloping sand layers, like the layers deposited by the wind on the faces of sand dunes. The difference is that this sand has been cemented into solid sandstone. So let's explore it, and you can try to convince me that your questions are justified.

CARL. Great idea. First off, this slab of rock above us provides inviting shade—a good place to eat lunch. I have shared other lunches in such places and enjoyed the discussions that can accompany the food.

ED. I just hope the discussions don't result in indigestion!

CARL. I like your sense of humor. But don't worry. I have a strong stomach. And I am usually not that irritating.

I have wondered why some scientists have so much confidence that the Coconino Sandstone formed in a desert. Many papers cite it as a classic eolian sandstone, but very few geologists actually come out here and study it. My colleagues and I find features in the sandstone that are not mentioned in the published research papers, apparently because there hasn't been much actual research. A few papers in the 1930s and 1940s described it as eolian, and their explanation became established as the correct answer.

I guess that isn't too surprising, because in its general appearance it looks like the sloping layers of sand that form on the downwind side of desert sand dunes. That is certainly what it looked like to me at first. I can understand why other geologists didn't see a good reason to doubt it. They didn't have sufficient motivation to question that explanation, so it continues to be the norm.

ED. That is how it appears to me. Do you think I am like the others, not asking the right questions? Science can't spend time questioning everything, and this looks so much like normal eolian sandstone.

CARL. It really is true that my religious views cause me to ask questions that might not seem necessary to others. I guess I am, in some ways, a skeptic. It has been said that the presence of a few independent-thinking mavericks in each generation keeps science from stagnating. Maybe I am one of those.

I don't mind that, especially since my unusual questions often have led me to new science-based findings.

ED. Hmm . . . but this rock has many of the characteristics of a desert dune deposit, so I am still doubtful. I am also bothered by publications by some creationists who clearly are not scientists. They not only reject evolution but don't know anything about the evidence. Aren't you embarrassed to be part of that group?

CARL. I know what you mean. I will be careful in answering that question, so as to not be misunderstood. I am embarrassed at their shallow misuse or ignorance of evidence, but I am still not ashamed to be known as a creationist. I have also heard evolutionists who were equally ignorant, but I don't equate you with those types. Although I disagree with you, I know you are not ignorant like them.

Leaving the slackers aside and coming back to the sandstone—one type of evidence that began to cause me to doubt the desert origin of the Coconino was in the fossil trackways, the only fossils in this formation. Down in this quarry, take a look at these tracks. They are either reptile or amphibian tracks. Some of the trackways move sideways, as if the animals were in the water, being drifted sideways by a current. The toes point one way, but the trackway is moving almost at a right angle to that. And look at these—they are not a series of right-left tracks, like in a normal trackway. They are just randomly placed individual footprints. In the many hours I have spent studying living animals and their tracks on sand dunes, I have never seen anything like this. I can only explain these tracks if the animals were swimming in the water and occasionally putting a foot down on the substrate.

ED. That's a logical idea, but I'm not ready to say it is the only possible explanation. How do other researchers explain these?

CARL. They don't. I have seen one published comment on tracks like these, and the author's attempt at interpretation didn't even acknowledge that there was something strange about the tracks. When I try to understand why he wouldn't notice the anomaly, I can suggest two possible reasons.

First, his prior commitment to the eolian interpretation kept him from seeing something worth considering in those tracks, because it could not fit his theory.

Second, he and some others are geologists who have never studied living animals, and thus they don't have the background to notice these details.

ED. And you think you have superior wisdom, so you saw what he didn't see?

CARL. I don't think I have superior wisdom. I do have a couple of probable, practical advantages. For one, my original graduate work in evolutionary biology involved the study of vertebrate animal behavior, before I trained in geology. Doing advanced study in two different fields is not doing things the easy way, but it did give me a broader background for understanding these fossils. My other advantage, the one that you and others may be doubtful about, is the result of my openness to both scientific insights and biblical ideas. Because of this, my thinking is open to a broader range of possibilities than is true of some others.

ED. That's an intriguing, although somewhat questionable, thought, but where in the Bible does it explain the Coconino Sandstone?

CARL. Here is where we should be careful to avoid indigestion! Even though the Bible writer Moses didn't know anything about the Coconino when he wrote the book of Genesis, my willingness to think the global flood was real opens my thinking to the possibility—the *possibility*, not requirement—that the Coconino formed in water. I want to figure out if it was or was not formed in water, and that can only be answered by careful science.

I suggest that neither the Bible nor proper open-minded science requires the Coconino Sandstone to be eolian, and neither requires it to be subaqueous, formed in water. Why is there such unbending commitment to the Coconino being eolian? Geology explains lots of other cross-bedded sandstones as formed in a subaqueous setting. I don't see why evolution-oriented geologists, even with their determination to leave the Bible out of their thinking, could not accept a subaqueous interpretation for the Coconino. There is something else going on here, other than the evidence or the legitimate requirements of geological theory.

Ed. One probable reason is that an eolian Coconino has had far-reaching implications in thinking about things like interpretations of ancient climate. Southwestern North America is seen as a dry, desert climate in the Permian period, because of the Coconino. If the Coconino gets reinterpreted, it would require a lot of rethinking of a number of geological ideas. There is resistance to that, not surprisingly. Your religious meddling in geology will probably add to that resistance.

Carl. I believe you're right about those things. But I need to finish explaining my general reason for my questioning attitude. I do agree with you that science can't spend time questioning everything. But I go further than many in thinking that if there is even a small reason to question an accepted theory, science will be benefited if some researchers broaden their thinking and develop alternate interpretations and seek to test them. That is what my research seeks to do.

Remember, my unconventional thinking results in *asking questions*. If we are interested in what science has to say about it, and I am, the *answers* to these questions must come from using scientific research procedures. Read my research papers and judge for yourself whether I do that.

Ed. You have published some good research papers. Are you ever willing to accept an answer that goes against your quirky thinking?

Carl. Ha, I still like your sense of humor! Some years ago, a paleobotanist and creationist friend wondered if there really were no fossil angiosperms, or flowering plants, below the Cretaceous, or if that idea was influenced by evolutionary theory. He and a graduate student studied fossil pollen in rocks below the Cretaceous, including one claim of angiosperm pollen in the Precambrian, and they were convinced that angiosperms really are not found below the Cretaceous—even though we puzzle over how this evidence fits into a biblical model of earth history. I agree with his approach.

Before we leave the Coconino, we need to look at one more piece of important evidence. Actually there is a lot more, but we'll just take time for this one. I have found several examples of fossil vertebrate trackways in the Coconino that either begin abruptly or end suddenly, with no evidence of sedimentary changes that could explain the strange trackways. These are not vague markings, but clear, distinct trackways that just end, suddenly and inexplicably. These are trackways of four-footed animals, with no wings. They did not fly away. So how, on a desert dune, could the animals suddenly vanish? There is one way to easily explain this evidence—and I think only one way. The animals swam underwater, walked on the sand, then swam away. I published this evidence, and so far none of the geologists who try to give eolian interpretations of my evidence have even mentioned these oddly ending tracks. No one has tried to explain them. I suspect it is because there is no other realistic explanation.

ED. My stomach isn't feeling good right now. I don't have an explanation either. But I will think of one! You can't be right about this.

CARL. Maybe a good meal this evening will help!

ED. Good idea. I've had enough roadkill. When we finish here at the rock quarry, let's move on toward the Grand Canyon. We should be able to find some answers to our questions there—and also find a delicious meal on the way, perhaps in Williams.

CHAPTER 4

A Story Unfolds

ED. Good morning. That was a great little local restaurant. Since it's sixty miles from Williams to the Grand Canyon, we have time to talk on the way. We have much more about geology that we can explore, but I would like to deal for a while with Darwin's transforming idea, biological evolution, since it is supported by such unquestionable evidence.

CARL. I'm fine with that. Evolution is a dominating idea in our culture. Do you agree that we can best understand an idea if we know the history of that idea?

ED. Knowing the history will certainly help, although I am not sure it is always critical. The relationship between a scientific idea and the evidence, I think, is the most important insight.

CARL. Perhaps the history is especially helpful for ideas that involve both evidence and assumptions. Theories of origins are in that category. Three centuries ago, just about everyone in the Western world was a creationist.

ED. Yes, those were days of ignorance, before Darwin brought new insights and the scholarly world learned to see how the universe really works and how it began.

CARL. I think the story needs to begin before Darwin, with changes in thinking that paved the way for Darwin's theory. The Middle Ages were an important part of the story. As that time period moved toward a close, the people, and especially scholars, were very weary of autocratic, domineering, and abusive government and religion. The Enlightenment brought a developing spirit of rebellion against both of those institutions. The Christian church of that era claimed the right to control the thoughts and actions of the public and even of kings, with death being a possible consequence for those who challenged that control. Many religious heretics learned that the hard way!

ED. Yes, and science suffered under that old domineering system. The theory of evolution didn't have a chance until that religious control ended, and that is why everyone back then was a creationist. You didn't dare be anything else. It isn't surprising that science has needed to shed its religious baggage. Of course, some of the great scientists of the past were creationists, like Kepler, Galileo, Linnaeus, and Newton. They hadn't learned the whole story yet.

CARL. Are you sure that is the only reason they were creationists?

ED. What other reason would there be?

CARL. Would Newton have accepted evolution if he had been contemporary with Darwin? We don't know the answer to that. A scientist who saw the wonder and regularity of the universe understood that there must be a Mind behind that.

ED. Careful—you are making an assumption. Now we know otherwise. This raises one very big question. It seems that you really do think there is a god. But how are the ideas of god and creation realistic in this modern, highly educated age? How can Creation be proposed as an acceptable, intelligent tale?

CARL. Many books have been written on those questions. I'll summarize a few critical points. First of all, study of physics and cosmology has revealed that the universe is finely tuned to support life. That is to say, the laws of physics are exactly right. If any of a number of important physical constants were slightly different, it would be impossible for life to exist. This concept results from scientific research, but it strongly implies that somebody who understands all of this designed and put together the universe. It seems that the only alternative offered by scientists is the wildly speculative, untestable, and, to me, unimpressive theory of multiple universes.

Second, remember our early discussion about how the first life began? The theory of abiogenesis has no scientific support. The rapidly escalating progress in understanding the biochemistry of living things is making it clear to many scientifically educated persons that life could not begin without intelligent design—there must be a designer of some kind. Objections to this idea have never included any reasonable alternatives, only unsupported assumptions. The intelligent design movement does not speak to the identity of the designer, but to fill out this topic, we can't avoid that issue.

Christians maintain that the God of the Bible is that Designer, and Jesus, the Son of God, lived on earth in human form for thirty-three years to better reveal the love of God for us and to redeem the fallen, sinful human race. This is explained in the Bible book of 1 Corinthians, chapter 15. The people of Jesus' time, however, were expecting a different kind of God, one who would support their pathetically self-centered religious beliefs, so they rejected Him and killed Him. But His resurrection showed that He really was God after all.

Ed. But it appears that His followers invented that fanciful, unrealistic version of the story later to make Jesus, their hero, look good. It's a great hero story, but not believable.

Carl. That's a common idea, but think about it. Jesus died a humiliating, very public death by the Roman method of crucifixion, while His closest followers ran away in fear. Would anyone invent a hero story like that? The participants looked very unheroic, until Jesus' resurrection changed their lives. Also, at that time, women held a very low position in society and were not considered reliable witnesses of anything. But some of Jesus' most faithful followers were women, and in the Bible the first witnesses of His resurrection were women. At that time, in that society, *nobody* would invent a story like that! The story has the ring of truth.

Parts of the New Testament were written down within a few decades after Jesus' death and resurrection. That is much too short a time for a fanciful legend to develop, especially when many eyewitnesses, who knew what really happened, were still alive. After Jesus returned to life, His fearful disciples were invigorated with new life and courage, and Christianity rapidly spread across the recognized world of that time. How could that possibly happen if the Bible story of Jesus, with His miracles and His resurrection, were false?

ED. You present a compelling story. But I can't help asking—if that story is true, why do so many intelligent, educated persons reject it? Can they all be wrong?

CARL. That is the age-old question: Do we accept human opinion, or do we believe what God has revealed to us?

ED. That is indeed a crucial question, and we will probably give different answers to it.

CARL. Yes, I presume we will.

ED. And there is another uncomfortable issue. Some have a belief in a god that leads them to use explosives to blow up other people, or to fly airplanes into buildings and kill thousands, and other horrific things too awful to think about. Religion leads to such violent, destructive behavior! How can you believe in a god in spite of all this?

CARL. I am as appalled at these things as you are. But what if there is a God who is even more appalled about these terrible things than we are, and also appalled at how badly humans misrepresent Him? Would that influence how you think about Him?

ED. You do have an imagination! I would have to think about this, but not now. Can we get back to our question of whether Newton would have accepted evolution if he lived today? The idea of a "Mind" behind the universe is an assumption. We don't know whether Newton would have held on to it.

CARL. Since we can't prove the existence of God, I guess it is an assumption, and the nature of assumptions and how they affect our thinking is an important part of the story we are exploring. It may not be as simple as it appears.

Part of the reaction against the old domineering institutions came in the form of philosophers who used their influence to deliberately wear down confidence in the old forms of authority, including the belief that the Bible is a divinely inspired, and thus trustworthy, book. The Bible began to be seen as just another unfortunate source of authority. They didn't recognize that the abuses of the church in the Middle Ages are not consistent with the Bible's message, and thus those abuses can't be blamed on the Bible.

ED. Perhaps there is something to what you are saying, but the new philosophical thinking was quite successful in formulating a new understanding, recognizing that we can think for ourselves without being under the thumb of ancient "authorities." This has led to great advances in science.

CARL. I agree with you. See, I am not always so stubborn! Where we probably disagree is whether the Bible was really in the same category as those other "authorities." And since modern science was in its infancy, scientists were not yet able to correctly understand a constructive relationship between faith and science.

ED. Well, I don't know about that. Those early scientists were Christians, and they were sure that God is always tinkering with nature and with the laws of nature. They thought that God's minute-by-minute actions keep our bodies working and keep the planets in their proper orbits, orbits that must be perfect circles, because that is how a perfect God would make them.

CARL. Again, I agree with your view of how those early scientists thought. For science to make real progress, it had to shed the idea that God is always tinkering with nature. But what they didn't realize is that this idea of God's tinkering came from their own minds, not from the Bible. The Bible doesn't deal with these details, but it is consistent with my belief that God is too awesome and organized to use such an inefficient system. He created a set of laws of chemistry and physics that is overwhelming in its completeness and effectiveness, and He maintains their constant, reliable operation. He uses these laws to operate the universe on a daily basis. There is normally no need for tinkering to keep the physical universe running properly, or even to keep the chemistry of our bodies working as intended.

ED. Ah, but you're forgetting that the Bible is full of stories of miracles—the claim of actions that violate the laws of nature. Science can't accept such magic, no matter how awesome your God is!

CARL. You are making assumptions again. The Bible is indeed full of miracles, but just what is magic? And how does it relate to the laws of chemistry and physics? I understand if you have trouble accepting this, but I suggest that God doesn't ever do magic, which to me means actions with no rational explanation that violate the laws of chemistry and physics. My biblical God is an organized, mathematically inclined super-scientist type. He doesn't violate the laws of physics and chemistry, because He doesn't need to. There is no need to go against those all-encompassing laws. He simply inserts the needed energy to change the course of events. We do things like that all the time. We make electrical gadgets designed to use energy to make things happen that would not happen otherwise, like making a garage door "magically" open! I think God could someday explain to us how He performed a miracle, and we might say, "Oh, now I understand how You did that."

I also think that God does miracles mainly in emergency situations; they are not the way He operates the universe on a daily basis. He does them because He loves us.

ED. That is clever reasoning, and you did have to throw in that "loving" part. Even though, as you recognize, I don't agree with your ideas, they do have a certain logic, up to a point. Theoretically there could be a God who operates that way. But the scientific evidence goes against that. And the miracles in the Bible aren't just healing sick people or raising the dead. I presume those are your "emergency situations." What about stories of God sending fire down in response to someone's prayer, collapsing the walls of a city, creating bread and fish to feed a multitude, and many other such episodes?

CARL. You're right. I realize that my term "emergency situations" is not an adequate explanation. The tinkering I was objecting to is the ancient concept that, for example, the kidneys, the heart, or the orbits of the planets require the daily special action of God or some kind of spirit to keep these processes working properly. No, those are not special miracles, they are the daily operation of God's natural laws. The divine actions in the Bible that we see as miracles are always God's actions in response to human needs and problems, and His seeking to interact with and encourage people to trust Him and to spread the good news about Him.

To a Christian, the physical universe and the laws of chemistry and physics are not the highest focus of God's attention. Those are very important, but they are just tools to support His highest concerns—rational beings, the relations between those beings, and their relationship with God Himself. Love really is what God values most! The biblical miracles are always directed to those highest concerns of our great God. I'm sure you recognize that many things in human relationships, and relations between cultures and nations, are not going well. We refer to this dysfunction as the problem of a sinful human race, and it is the major part of that emergency situation that God responds to with miracles, although I still think that if we knew enough we could see that God uses His laws, rather than miracles, in doing even these things. They are not irrational magic as I have defined it.

ED. So you are saying that God's miracles are not done to make planets, gravity, kidneys, biochemistry, or electrical currents work properly. They are done to help humans deal with damaged relationships. Is this the basic idea? OK, that generally fits, but the Bible also says that God created life instantly, and that is where all life came from. How do you justify that idea? Why would your God not do it in a more scientifically realistic way?

CARL. I will answer with an illustration from our life experience. We can make devices that use the laws of physics to open a garage door, but those same laws won't *create* a garage door. An intelligent inventor is required. The same is true for life. A living cell is an incredibly complex mechanism, made to operate by normal laws of biochemistry, but those laws cannot make a living cell appear out of a random mix of nonliving molecules. A century of biochemical research supports that. And you might take a look at James Tour's lecture video on YouTube, called "The Origin of Life: An Inside Story." To begin life requires a special event, like only an awesome God could do!

We could spend hours with this interesting discussion, but can we move on with our story of history?

ED. Please. This is getting in too deep, heading toward more indigestion!

CARL. I suggest that as scholars studied more and more aspects of nature and the physical universe, and they realized that they are governed by laws rather than micromanaged by God's arbitrary tinkering, they carried this concept too far and applied it to the origin of life and of the physical universe. They not only ended belief in God's daily "tinkering," but they also decided that the universe did not need a creator.

ED. That is correct. They got rid of the God-of-the-gaps thinking, which needed God to explain things we couldn't explain without some outside help. Some biologists in the 1800s liked this naturalistic thinking but still had a problem with the origin of life, because life did seem to need a creator. Some wrote books suggesting an evolution of life-forms, and finally Charles Darwin put together a more developed theory of evolution that was a success, moving God to the scrap heap.

CARL. There is one little twist in this story. Darwin's theory of natural selection was not accepted by many biologists for a number of decades, but his theory was successful for a *philosophical* reason—it convinced his supporters that they could find a way to explain life's origins without the need for an unwanted creator.

As we look backward from the twenty-first century, we recognize that Darwin lived at a time when almost nothing was known about the nature of life. A cell was understood as a little bag with some simple contents that could easily evolve. Even the field of genetics was decades in the future. Let me suggest to you a scenario that I think is correct, though unwelcome to many scientists.

I suggest that Darwinian evolution, with its development of the many forms of life by random mutations and natural selection, has become so solidly entrenched in scientific thinking and education that it is assumed, and not questioned, even though current scientific knowledge makes Darwinian theory incompatible with the evidence.

ED. I doubt the validity of your last point about the evidence. Are you denying that random mutations and natural selection are supported by a whole lot of evidence? Fortunately, we have reached our hotel at the Canyon! That will give me more time to put together a convincing response to your creative thinking.

CHAPTER 5

Microevolution and Certainty

ED. Today, let's just hike and enjoy the Grand Canyon.

CARL. The magnificent scenery may shake loose some helpful insights!

ED. It puzzles me why so many people, even scientists, object to evolution. Your doctorate from Cornell University was in evolutionary biology, right? And yet you believe in Creation!

CARL. Correct. That was my field of study. They gave me a good education in evolution and also in ecology.

ED. Aren't they now embarrassed that they gave a PhD to a creationist? And after the education you received, how can you still doubt evolution?

CARL. Actually my guidance committee knew I was a creationist, but they—or at least my mentor, my guidance committee chairman—knew that my master's thesis was on speciation in white-footed mice, which of course is included in evolution. So he knew that I didn't just unthinkingly reject evolution. In fact, he recommended that I write up part of my thesis and submit it for the "best student paper" competition at the national meetings of the Mammalogy Society. I didn't have any objections back then, and I don't have any now, to the reality of microevolution and the development of new species.

I don't know of any biologically educated creationist who doubts those areas of evolution theory. That level of biological change is supported by a very large amount of evidence. If you read carefully and listen carefully, most of the evidence that evolutionary biologists give in support of evolution is actually just evidence for evolutionary change within species and changes up to about the level of new genera. That is where evolution is strong. The problems for evolution begin to multiply when trying to explain macroevolution, which is evolutionary origin of families, orders, classes, and phyla of organisms. That is the battleground between creationists and noncreationists.

ED. That changes the picture somewhat. By the way, how did it go at the mammalogy meetings?

CARL. I did get the best student paper award. They liked my research, and that wasn't the last such award that has been given to a creationist.

ED. What you explained about microevolution and speciation is helpful, but still, how can you justify making that distinction between microevolution and macroevolution? Isn't the latter just an extension of the former? The random mutations, with the help of natural selection, just keep adding up until they eventually lead to an entirely different kind of animal. That is solid science.

CARL. That's what the majority of evolutionary biologists accept. A growing number of scientists, however, are having doubts that macroevolution is just an extension of microevolution. But before we get bogged down in that controversy, let's look at some of the evidence that supports small-scale evolution. I prefer that term instead of microevolution; it's a simpler and more biologically meaningful term that can be used instead of referring to microevolution plus speciation. Small-scale evolution, as I use the term, includes all or most changes below the family level, approximately.

ED. I'm not sure about that idea. Species is a more clearly defined category than genus, family, and so on, so it seems logical to put microevolution, which is change within a species, in one category, and any change above the species level in the other category. What is your justification for dividing it at the family level? Examples of species are things like the red fox, the western fence lizard, or the American robin. We generally can recognize a species when we see a familiar one. A family is a more diverse grouping that may not mean much to an ordinary person. For example, the Mustelidae family includes wolverines, weasels, badgers, and otters. Make sense of that one!

CARL. You're right about that. When I teach a mammalogy class I tell the students to think of the family Mustelidae as the "other" family. If the mammal doesn't seem to fit in a familiar family like bears, dogs, cats, or rodents, they are probably right to put it in the family Mustelidae!

The reason for dividing evolution as I suggest is that the process involved in adaptations within a species, microevolution, is not really different from the process that results in the changes that define different genera. An example of a genus is the group that includes several species of woodrats—genus *Neotoma*. Species of *Neotoma* are different in size and in other minor features of anatomy, physiology, and ecology. These are the same types of features that make a woodrat different from a white-footed mouse. Changing a mouse into a woodrat would not require the evolution of any new organs or new physiological systems. The changes would be minor and would probably not require any significant new genes. And the evolution of a new species is simply the result of small microevolutionary changes that happen to prevent two populations from interbreeding.

This contrasts with macroevolution, which could be called large-scale evolution. For example, for a reptile to evolve into a mammal, which is a new class, it would require the evolution of a more complex brain, the system of live birth, warm-blooded physiology, and other extremely complex features, with *many* new gene complexes. That is a completely different task than small-scale evolution.

ED. OK, I see your logic, whether or not I agree with it. I think there is a lot of evidence that those small-scale evolution processes are genuine, beyond any reasonable doubt.

CARL. Any evolutionary biologist will agree with that, as well as creationists who have studied biology. In this part of evolution theory I would say there is certainty about the basic concept. That is true even though we can almost never see a new species appear! But the evidence that animals and plants change as they adapt to environmental variation can be observed, and the indirect evidence for evolution of new species is too abundant to be questioned.

I'll mention one classic research experience showing adaptation by evolution. Darwin's finches in the Galapagos Islands have either heavy or slender beaks, according to the seeds that they habitually eat. In recent decades, a drought affected the type of seeds that were available to the birds. As the average seed size got larger, the birds with larger beaks survived better and became relatively more abundant. Then, when the drought ended, the finch beak sizes averaged smaller again. This was clearly small-scale evolution, microevolution, in action.

These are exactly the results evolution would predict. There was, however, one part of the results that is surprising, compared to classic evolution theory. The surprise is how fast these changes, and others that have been studied, occur. It used to be thought that small-scale evolutionary change took thousands of years. Recent research has resulted in recognition that these adaptations can occur rapidly, in a human lifetime, or even in the time of one research project. Careful research like that is what brings such certainty in the theory of small-scale evolution.

In fact, when evolutionary scientists present arguments that evolution, including macroevolution, is true, the evidence they often use is actually just evidence for this small-scale evolution.

ED. Are you sure? Why would they do something so dumb? That sounds like a typical creationist straw-man argument.

CARL. I don't think evolutionary scientists are dumb! In fact, I have good friends in that group, and they are typically very capable and well informed. The problem isn't lack of intelligence or knowledge. They use bad arguments—believe it or not—because they don't understand creationists!

ED. Come on, now, this is getting strange! What do you mean, they don't understand creationists?

CARL. If I'm trying to convince you that Fords are better than Toyotas, but I have never studied or driven any Toyotas, I could make some very poor arguments, no matter how much I know about Fords. That is the problem. A person who doesn't know what or how creationists think, and who may even wonder if they think at all, has not had to carefully consider what is the difference between a creationist theory of change and Darwinian theory. It seems to me that the certainty resulting from the abundant evidence for small-scale adaptations gives awesome confidence in evolution. But most evolutionary scientists have not been pushed to analyze whether this type of evidence really supports macroevolution as well.

I will even make a statement that I don't think you will like. I suggest that my students, whom I have required to understand both the standard evolution theory and a creationist theory of origins, can have a better understanding of Darwinian theory than many conventional evolutionary biologists. My students have been pushed to learn about both "Fords" and "Toyotas" in science, and the result is that they are prepared to think about both and to recognize what evidence actually does favor one over the other.

That is the difference. We are prepared to make comparisons and call them valid only if we thoroughly understand the things we are comparing. I read a lot in the anticreationist literature. It seems clear to me that the scientists who write that material have little or no understanding of how the biologically educated creationists think. The consequence is that they often say foolish things in their anticreationist books and have a superficial view of how evidence relates to theories. I suggest that nobody should write either anti-creationist or anti-evolution books or articles unless they have studied both and have at least one good, well-informed friend in the group they are arguing against. That would at least soften a lot of empty rhetoric.

ED. Even if you are confused about macroevolution, you do at least seem to grasp what microevolution and speciation are about. And there is some validity in what you say about the arguments over evolution. We probably do need to improve our understanding of what creationists think, in order to do a better job of showing how wrong you are.

CARL. Touché!

This overlook is a great place to eat our lunch. I remember, years ago, hiking down to the bottom of the canyon with a student. Other times I just hiked down to the Coconino Sandstone, near the top of the canyon, to study the fossil tracks, while my colleague had to hike all the way down to the Cambrian. I was sure I had made the right choice of research project!

ED. Yes—the practical choice! And this sandwich is delicious.

CARL. Was there ever a time in your life when you thought there might be a God, or when you even read the Bible?

ED. Oh, yes. As a kid I was part of a Christian family. We regularly went to church and learned all the Bible stories. I was a true believer, and life was good.

CARL. What influenced you to change?

ED. In school I began to learn about evolution. I didn't pay much attention to it, but by the time I reached college it became too convincing to ignore the implications, and even more convincing by the time I finished graduate school. All that the science teachers gave us was built on the theory of evolution, which I could no longer reconcile with what I had learned in church and at home. I could no longer accept those quaint beliefs from an old book. Some Christians try to weave macroevolution into their religious beliefs, but that didn't make sense to me. The logic of those two ideas doesn't fit together. I am with Jerry Coyne in the conclusion that religion and evolution don't have any connection with each other. So that is what brought me to where I am now.

CARL. Your early life was happy, but that was not the experience of some former Christians. They have very negative memories of their home and religious life.

ED. I know some who are like that. I guess I was fortunate to be in a loving, sensible Christian family. At the time it all made sense to me.

CARL. Look at those condors flying past. They are so magnificent! Coming back to your description of your early life—do you ever think about that and miss that experience you had as a child?

ED. There are dark moments when I think back on that time and miss it and even wish it was a true experience. But I can no longer believe in lies, no matter how comforting those fables might be.

Fortunately, my family is still loving, and they seem to accept my choice and still care about me.

CARL. The God I know also highly values our freedom of choice. His entire approach to relating to the human race is based on the importance of that freedom of choice.

ED. If I could believe a God like that was really there, it might still have some appeal. But that doesn't square with what science has taught us. And I'm affected by those episodes of mass murder by people whose God tells them to do it. I can't be satisfied with sweet, false answers to the big questions of life.

If you don't mind, I would like to hike alone today. Nostalgia is interfering with my objectivity, and I need to clear my mind.

CARL. I understand. I will see you tomorrow morning.

CHAPTER 6

Deep Time

ED. That was a very good breakfast, and after having time yesterday to collect my thoughts, I am ready to go again. These Grand Canyon cooks know what they're doing. They must not be creationists!

It seems that we do agree on one thing at least. A lot of evolution happens within and between species. I still see some big problems. If the Bible story of Creation were true, then the history of life on earth, the time since about the beginning of the Cambrian, would have to be only thousands of years, not 541 million years. Is that not correct? How do you reconcile that with the evidence? For example, this impressive set of rock layers here in the Grand Canyon—and this is only the Paleozoic! The rest of the geological column is above this, to the north in Arizona and Utah.

CARL. There is indeed a lot of rock, but what types of evidence convince you that the 541 million years is correct?

ED. Obviously radiometric dates are the strongest evidence. That data systematically nails down the age of rocks, right up through the geological column, with an ever-increasing level of accuracy.

CARL. I will grant you that one, at least most of it. Creationists have done some interesting work on this, but I still don't really know how to explain it. But what other evidence do you have?

ED. You seem to be implying that the radiometric dates are not enough! You are asking for more evidence? The radiometric dating is based directly on well-understood principles of physics, and that is solid science.

CARL. That could seem to be the end of the story, unless other evidence contradicts the radiometric timescale, for at least the time since the Cambrian. There is such evidence, and so even though I don't have a convincing answer for the radiometric dates, we seem to have reasons to keep an open mind and keep examining many lines of evidence.

As you probably suspect, I also have biblical reasons for not just taking the accepted dates at face value. I am willing to predict, based on what God has revealed, that as serious scientific research continues, it will become more evident that the radiometric data mean something different than the current interpretation. I suggest they are giving us important systematic information but not telling us the time in years for the geological column.

ED. You can't be serious! You are risking having science prove that the Bible is wrong, and that would destroy all your religious faith. Since your faith is such a big thing in your life, what happens then? You are betting your career on the risky idea that some mythical "God" knows more than scientists do.

CARL. Would I want to maintain faith in something that turned out to be false? No. The Bible, and my experience with it, gives me many reasons to have confidence in what it says, and I am not threatened by the possibility that I may not always have all the answers. I'm quite sure I could not adequately convince you, in this short time we have together, that my biblical faith is justified. I have sufficient reasons for that faith, however, so I will use it as the foundation for searching for scientific answers to my questions, with confidence that it will be a fruitful search. That doesn't mean that all my personal ideas will turn out to be correct. After all, when I apply what the Bible says in my examination of scientific theories, I am *interpreting* how to do that. It is a human endeavor. I may not get it all correct, but I'm confident that this approach will lead to new insights, supported by a closer look at the evidence. It already has.

I don't use science to test the accuracy of the Bible. I believe our human experience is too limited to justify that. Rather, I allow the Bible to help me ask better questions in my scientific searching—questions that we would otherwise probably not think of.

ED. Thinking of new constructive questions is certainly beneficial. But beyond that, I think I am in deep water, way over my head! But let's keep looking and talking. Maybe I can yet put some sense into your head.

CARL. You can keep trying! I don't mind. As I said, it is not threatening to me for someone to disagree with me. I will also try to convince you that I have something worthwhile to share.

I have trouble reconciling several types of evidence with a millions-of-years timescale. One is the abundant biochemicals, like proteins, found in fossils dated at tens or even hundreds of millions of years old. Something seems to be wrong there.

Other evidence comes from geology. Conventional theory claims that the ancient rock formations, all through the geological column, were produced slowly by essentially the same geological processes we observe occurring on earth today, like rivers depositing mud or sand. And yet as I examine those rocks I see features that are just too out of harmony with the slow, usually gradual modern processes. But maybe we should begin with the old biochemicals.

ED. OK, those are fascinating. It is amazing how those proteins have lasted for so many millions of years.

CARL. Publications since early in the twentieth century have been reporting proteins in ancient fossils, but the work that really began turning heads was done in North Carolina by Mary Schweitzer. She found the protein collagen in dinosaur bone, from the Cretaceous. The tissue was not mineralized—it was still protein that was even stretchy. She also found little red objects that seemed to be red blood cells in blood vessels. Others had a hard time accepting this evidence. Some claimed the evidence must be the result of modern bacteria in the fossils. Schweitzer's findings were so unexpected because research on modern proteins shows that the amino acids in proteins are destroyed by natural processes in thousands of years—so how could they be more than sixty million years old? Schweitzer said her favorite response by a reviewer of one of her manuscripts was the statement, "I don't care what the evidence is, I don't believe it."

ED. That reviewer didn't express himself very well, but he had a valid point. We know how old the fossils are, from the radiometric dates. The age is not in question, so something has to be wrong with the biochemical research. Does Mary Schweitzer think the fossils are only a few thousand years old?

CARL. No, she accepts the old age for the fossils. She still believes the biochemical evidence and has used additional methods to verify that the tissue is really from the dinosaur. Her evidence is strong, and she evidently thinks there must be an answer for the seeming conflict between the date and the existence of the proteins. When two lines of evidence are in conflict, this tells us something will be discovered that will resolve the conflict. Think of this situation as an opportunity—a clue that discovery is awaiting the serious researcher who diligently pursues the challenge of finding the answer to this puzzle.

ED. I like that. Scientific progress is all about accepting challenges and following up on clues. The things we know for sure, like the ages of the rocks, will tell us when we need to look elsewhere for the answer to the challenge.

CARL. This also tells us there should be room in science for different ideas about what is known "for sure." We discussed why science does not provide absolute truth but only evaluates different models and helps us see which model fits the *currently available* evidence. What if the real problem is in our understanding of the radiometric evidence? And everyone is only *assuming* that the solution to this puzzle is in finding how biochemicals can last millions of years? What if there is surprising evidence about radiometric processes waiting to be discovered? I think you will say that is ridiculous, but what if I am right about this? Some creationists are pursuing research for answers to these questions.

ED. Certainly you are wrong, and why would a scientist spend his or her time pursuing questions like doubts about these dates, when they're confident that the research will lead nowhere?

CARL. They shouldn't spend their time doing that. Motivation and insight will come to a person who's pursuing research they believe in, so if new data on radiometric processes is to be discovered, it will most likely be found by someone who does the research because they believe in it; they believe there might be new data to be discovered. If they do make a breakthrough—find a theory that better explains the radiometric data—an important next step follows. Then we want to know if their discovery is real or just a result of their careless thinking. At that stage in the study, it is best if some scientists are willing to look at the question from different sides. When they do so, their interaction will in time reveal which interpretation stands up to critical tests of their opposing ideas. The correctness of a theory is best revealed if it has to stand up to serious challenges. Are those who believe in the accuracy of radiometric dates willing to accept such a challenge, or will they stand on their assumptions and reject challenges to their favored dating methods out of hand?

ED. OK, fair enough. Perhaps someone will accept the challenge and show that the fossils really are that old. Now I'll throw one of your questions back at you. You propose that these ancient biochemicals are evidence that contradict the deep time scale. Is this all you have? Or do you have other such evidence to share?

CARL. Actually, I have only just begun! The other arguments against deep time will be geological. Some of these directly address time, and others imply that conventional geology theory doesn't work in general.

By "conventional theory" I mean the idea that modern geological processes, extended through time, produced the ancient rock formations. For example, fluvial sediments were deposited by flowing water—rivers, streams, or floods. This part of the interpretation we will probably all agree on. The big question is whether the ancient deposits resulted over deep time by the types of flowing water systems we observe today, or whether they developed rapidly by much larger-scale, more catastrophic processes. Some of us see evidence in the rocks that seems to indicate a lot of those large-scale, catastrophic events. In fact, sometimes when we examine the sedimentary rocks we ask ourselves, "Where in this series of sedimentary layers can those millions of years fit?" This is the topic of geology research by creationists.

ED. I see. You're thinking they were deposited by the global flood?

CARL. I would consider that possibility, at least for a number of formations, but science can't readily test such a big concept as the global flood. What we can do is ask, for each rock formation, "Does the evidence here indicate a slow, gradual fluvial process, or a large-scale, more rapid process?" And in many cases when I say "largescale," I mean that it looks as though some process deposited sediment over hundreds or thousands of square miles, instead of a few meters or square miles, as in modern river systems. If you're game, we could go look at some of these phenomena.

ED. This excursion is growing more expansive! But why not? I'm willing to have my doubts about your flood confirmed, which will certainly happen.

I guess we will have to leave the Grand Canyon, but I look forward to more adventures.

CARL. We can do some serious driving and examine a few of those geographically widespread rock formations and compare them to the modern processes believed to have formed them.

ED. This should be an experience! I'm sure you can't be right and so many other geologists wrong. Your evidence will need to be really good.

CARL. That's a challenge I can't refuse. My experience of traveling western North America in study of its awesome geology with my students over four decades and publishing research papers from our geology and paleontology investigations has raised many questions and suggested some answers that I find convincing.

Of the many rock formations we could choose, we might as well start with one of the really widespread ones—the Upper Jurassic Morrison Formation. This formation is understood to be primarily the result of rivers and floodplains, with part of it deposited in lakes or swampy areas, and it contains many animal fossils, including abundant dinosaurs, but few plant fossils. It is sandstone, siltstone, mudstone, and limestone, and it has colorful layers that vary from gray to red or purple to green.

It will be good to review what is meant by a rock formation. When a geologist identifies a specific body of sandstone, for example, he or she follows that sandstone across the landscape to determine how far it extends. At one end it may go underneath other rocks, so it isn't possible to follow it farther.

Ed. That's right. We can only know how far it goes if we can find evidence of it. The geologist can see that this body of sediment, with identifiable characteristics, occurs over a defined geographic area. It may be that a similar sandstone formation is found forty miles away, but if it can't be determined that it is the same body of sandstone, it will be named as a different formation. Is it really a different body of sand, or did it just change somewhat in the intervening forty miles, where it was not visible on the surface? That is a judgment the geologist will need to make.

Carl. That's a good description of the process of identifying and naming formations. It's an important element in geology research, but it does have some limitations.

Ed. The Morrison Formation is truly a famous deposit of dinosaurs. It is also in many places very colorful, as you mentioned, because of the volcanic ash that it contains. I have always found it to be a great source of wonder and of instructive fossil evidence.

CHAPTER 7

Questions About Deep Time

CARL. We are now in Colorado, after a whirlwind tour of parts of the Morrison Formation in several states. Let's review what we saw. In northern Texas, the Morrison Formation contains sandstone but is largely shale, red to bluish in color. And it has the usual dinosaurs. You remember the outcrop we saw?

Then we traveled west very fast to see some of the Morrison in New Mexico, and we didn't get any speeding tickets. We saw a Morrison outcrop in northeastern Arizona, and didn't it look familiar?

ED. The geology is awesome, but I'm not sure what it's telling us.

CARL. Hang on, and it will become clearer before we are done. In eastern Utah, near the tourist town of Moab, the Morrison outcrops yield plenty of material for the shops that sell fossils, and the rocks are typical Morrison Formation.

You recall the sweeping river and floodplain deposit in Montana, not far from Canada? We found the same Morrison with its dinosaurs there. How many rivers are there that spread sediment over such a large area?

ED. It is a long way, but think of how long the Mississippi River is. Certainly it goes farther than we traveled. You haven't convinced me yet of the catastrophic flood.

CARL. We aren't done yet! The Missouri-Mississippi River system is very long, but it is a ribbon of river sediment and doesn't spread its sediment over an area five hundred miles wide. But someone might suggest that such a Jurassic river ribbon just turned a wide corner from Montana and went east, so let's keep considering what we saw and find out if we were following a ribbon of sediment deposit or a vast, wide area of it.

We saw Morrison in South Dakota, Nebraska, and Kansas. And now we're in central Colorado, where the formation was first named.

ED. This dinosaur bed is enormous! These ancient river systems were huge, very different from the rivers we have now. But that's just the way it was. I don't see that Noah had anything to do with it.

CARL. Nice sarcasm! As we said before, science can't tell us whether Noah was involved; we can only look at the rocks we see and try to understand the processes that put them there. You're right about the ancient river systems being *very* different from rivers on our earth now. Think about that observation you made and what it means. The Jurassic "rivers" were not just different; they were radically, fundamentally different! Look at this area we have been through— parts of Texas, New Mexico, Arizona, and Nevada; all over Utah, Colorado, Wyoming, and Montana; western North Dakota, South Dakota, Nebraska, and Kansas! We find no evidence of any large rivers in the Morrison. The Morrison Formation covers at least six hundred thousand square miles! A deposit made by flowing water from Canada to Texas and from the slot machines of Las Vegas, Nevada, to central Nebraska—what does that tell us?

ED. I see that I share one problem with you—I don't know how to explain some things. I just know that science must begin with some basic assumptions in order to function. We can't allow God to be involved, with His Creation and Flood stories. The laws of nature can't be violated and still allow science to reach unbiased conclusions.

CARL. We do want unbiased conclusions, but could it be possible that even agnostic or atheist assumptions could bring their own biases? Why can we not just look at this vast Morrison, with its system of moving water, and, with our minds open to various options, recognize the possibility that the evidence may indicate a catastrophic event that was *very* different from what happens on earth now? The laws of nature were not different. Water never did flow uphill. But the circumstances were very different, and it is tough to try to explain the Morrison sediments by an extension of modern rivers and streams through deep time.

Time does not perform miracles, and I suggest it would be close to a miracle for observed modern processes to spread this relatively uniform deposit over such an area for millions of years. We live in a world with modern landscape that is a collage of valleys, hills, mountains, gullies, and rivers running in channels. That is what modern geological processes do. Since water did not ever flow uphill, how did this six-hundred-thousand-square-mile Morrison flood happen unless a vast catastrophe flattened the land and set the stage for the rapid deposit of the Morrison Formation over a relatively uniform surface?

ED. The Morrison Formation is indeed unique. I suppose an unusual event like this could happen, but this is just one formation. What about the rest? Many formations must be different from the Morrison.

CARL. I'm glad you asked. The widespread, flat-lying nature of the Morrison is not unique but is actually quite typical of the Paleozoic and Mesozoic sedimentary formations. Since we are here in Colorado, let's take a side trip back to Utah and look at another formation—the Upper Triassic Shinarump Formation. That is a very uniform deposit of sand and rounded pebbles, like the pebbles you could find in a streambed. Pebbles like this don't just randomly exist; they were rounded by being bounced against one another in a flowing river or stream.

Later that day . . .

CARL. We see the Shinarump here at the top of the cliff, west of St. George, Utah. You can see the sharp, continuous contact of the Shinarump with the Moenkopi Formation below it. The Shinarump usually is at the top of a cliff, because it is such hard rock that it doesn't erode easily. The softer Moenkopi erodes more easily, but the hard Shinarump holds up the cliff. We don't have the time or money to charter a helicopter, but if we did so and flew along that cliff, which I have done, all the way across Utah and into northwest Arizona, we would see how persistent and extensive the Shinarump is. And it doesn't stop there. It goes southeast through New Mexico and north through much of Utah and eastern Nevada, into Colorado, and maybe into Texas.

Creation? Really?

ED. I have heard of the Shinarump. It is interpreted as a braided stream deposit. Braided streams flow fast enough to carry pebbles like these as well as sand. Thus, braided streams carry the type of sediment we find in the Shinarump, which explains how the sand and pebbles got here.

CARL. Yes, but something important is missing from your explanation. Think of what braided streams are like in the modern world. The problem with the braided stream interpretation arises if we think about braided streams in the context of what is around them. The stream flows in a stream channel and erodes into whatever makes up the ground where it is. The path of the stream may change through time, but will it uniformly spread sand and pebbles over a vast area? If we could cut a trench across a modern braided stream channel, and perhaps make the trench a mile long, we could see what kind of deposit a braided stream will produce. We would find complex, nonuniform sediments along the length of that trench, rather than uniform sand and pebbles. There would be patches of sand and pebbles separated by patches of mud or soil. That is in striking contrast to the uniform nature of the Shinarump, which is sand and pebbles, about fifty to one hundred feet thick, covering more than one hundred thousand square miles! How do you spread a sheet of sand and pebbles uniformly over such an area? In a world like the one we live in, it just doesn't even begin to happen that way!

And since streams with such coarse material in them have power to erode, why didn't the Shinarump streams, over millions of years, erode away the mud or sand in the softer formations below them?

ED. That's another question I can't answer. I still know that science cannot accept mythology, and that is what you are bringing into this conversation! Why are other geologists not thinking the way you do? Why are they not bringing major catastrophes into their explanations? It seems like you folks are alone in this.

CARL. We are. Why is that? Is it because of the evidence? Or is it because of philosophy and assumptions? We all make philosophical choices, and they affect what evidence we notice and take seriously. The philosophy and assumptions I am questioning are part of the concept of methodological naturalism—or MN. If we accept MN, it doesn't allow us to ask questions that could challenge deep time and gradualistic geological processes. Science dominated by MN limits the types of questions that can be asked. But what if MN is not correct? And it isn't apparent to me that the evidence is on your side.

CHAPTER 8

Macroevolution—A Certainty?

ED. All this travel is tiring, and the geology is perplexing. I suggest we sit under some juniper trees and talk about something else, like macroevolution. That is where you have a lot of problems! Biologists know how mammals, dinosaurs, beetles, and fish came to be. They were not invented by some creator but evolved through immense time. Even the puzzling Morrison Formation can't erode that fact; and it is a fact!

Early in this trip you suggested that a growing number of scientists are having doubts that macroevolution is just an extension of microevolution. Some are, but even if we don't know for sure how macroevolution works, the fact of such evolution remains. I will be intrigued to see how you deal with that. The fossil record begins with simple organisms, and they get more complex and varied as the millions of years of evolution roll on.

CARL. I admire your confidence, even as I doubt that its foundation is as sure as you believe it is.

ED. How can the foundation be uncertain? Evolutionary biologists can make phylogenetic trees that show which animals evolved from which others. The entire army of evolutionary biologists at universities around the world agree that Darwinism, the understanding that all organisms evolved through random mutations and natural selection, is the only explanation for the origin of all these organisms.

CARL. Darwinism is indeed the accepted explanation if we assume there was no creator. But those phylogenetic trees all require the assumption that the similarities between different organisms resulted from evolution from common ancestors, rather than similarity because of a common designer. This is the philosophical choice we have to make, but let's leave that aside and discuss evidence.

In Darwin's day, nothing at all was known about genetics and molecular biology, but the frequency of new discoveries in those areas has been going through the ceiling in recent years. Those are the fields that deal directly with whatever *process* of evolution is occurring. I also notice that it is scientists in molecular biology and genetics who are now quite vocally expressing doubts about random mutation and natural selection. Maybe something is there that we should pay attention to, no matter what assumptions we prefer.

ED. Those guys are sitting in their laboratories and not in touch with the real world of natural history! If they were, they would understand evolution. One of the clearest cases is the loss of eyes by animals living in caves. Mutations damage their eyes, and since they don't need eyes in the darkness of the caves, natural selection does not eliminate those individuals with those mutations. But some animals living out in the daylight no doubt get those same mutations, and natural selection weeds out the damaged individuals. That is evolution in action, and you can't argue with that!

CARL. You are again using microevolution as a general argument for evolution, but I will let you get away with it to address the bigger issue.

I used to teach my students exactly what you describe. I also sometimes tell my students that half of what we teach them is wrong. But we don't know which half is wrong until science moves on and makes more discoveries. This is just such a case. Recent research has found that the blind cave fish don't have mutations to their eye genes. The eye genes are intact, but molecular systems outside of the DNA, recently discovered, manage how the DNA is interpreted. This is called epigenetics—control systems outside of or above the DNA. Epigenetics is a rapidly growing field of study and is revolutionizing the understanding of genetics. The environment—the dark cave—was somehow sensed by the fish's molecular sensors, and little epigenetic markers turned off the eye genes. Epigenetic signals and markers manage a lot of other aspects of genetics, and in this process the internal molecular systems of animals and plants sense the environment and initiate beneficial nonmutational genetic changes that can be inherited.

ED. Wait a minute! That sounds like serious heresy. I know they don't burn heretics anymore, but you are on dangerous intellectual ground. If internal genetic sensors can initiate beneficial, heritable changes, someone or something knows how to determine what the animal needs and make the necessary changes. That sounds like some kind of magic. Who is the genie doing that—the tooth fairy? Darwin understood that all biological changes must begin with random genetic events. If they are not random, then someone is messing with the system. Even if you believe in your Creator God, it sounds like He is tinkering with genetics at each step of life, and you said you don't believe that. So how do you explain this?

CARL. I don't believe God is tinkering, and such tinkering is not necessary to explain epigenetics. Epigenetics is solid science, supported by an increasing amount of evidence. It seems that the Creator knew, before He designed the biochemical and genetic systems, that organisms would face challenges in their lives and would need to be able to adapt to changes in their environments. He made the molecular system so it could sense what the environment was like and adjust accordingly, without any tinkering needed. So as I understand it, the explanation for all the amazing genetic and other molecular systems is in their original design, not in daily tinkering, even by the tooth fairy! The Creator was wise enough to make a mechanism that works.

ED. If this is all true, why is the world of evolutionary biologists not accepting it? I don't see any of this in the newest evolution textbooks.

CARL. You are right, but only partly right. The standard evolution texts ignore or downplay new molecular discoveries like epigenetics. The molecular biologists, the ones who really know what is going on in the genetic system, point out that evolutionary biologists are ignoring three decades of molecular biology research. The evolutionary biologists object to the findings of this research, but according to the molecular biologists, this objection is philosophical, not scientific, and is not supported by empirical evidence. By the way, the molecular biologists I am referring to are not creationists; they just recognize that Darwin was wrong.

ED. If what you are saying is true, this could lead to war among scientists.

CARL. The "war" has already begun! The reason I say you are only partly right is that a group of evolutionary biologists—who are not creationists—recognize that epigenetics is real, and they are developing an alternate evolution theory, called the extended synthesis, utilizing epigenetic insights. At a recent conference, a confrontation arose between conventional evolutionary biologists and advocates of the extended synthesis. Individuals who were at the conference concluded that the conventional thinkers did not answer the issues raised by the proponents of the extended synthesis but just insisted that selection was an adequate explanation. I propose that epigenetic discoveries help us see how small-scale evolution works rapidly and effectively to quickly adapt organisms to their environment, just as creationists have been saying all along.

One conclusion from that conference that I agree with was that neither group had a workable explanation of how new structures arose—novelties like bones, eyes, kidneys, the vertebrate limbs or wings, or hands that can skillfully play a violin. Natural selection only eliminates bad features. It does nothing, *nothing at all*, to originate a new structure, a new gene, or an adaptation of some structure.

These new things, in evolution, can originate only by a long sequence of specific genetic changes, but those changes must occur *randomly*, and such a new structure has to be mostly complete before natural selection can even recognize it. For many of us who are aware of the molecular awesomeness of living things, this is simply not credible.

And some of those features are not even necessary for survival. They are bonus features, like many abilities of the human brain. Though not creationists, even some of the molecular-biologist critics of Darwinism don't know how to explain life and the diversity of life-forms. They simply say it is a mystery. I think they are the honest ones.

ED. Some of those things are a puzzle. I don't know the answers. And there are also puzzles for you, if you face it honestly. For example, what about a big category of evidence, which we haven't talked about yet, that requires evolution to explain the data? Like Hox genes, which control embryonic development, putting the parts of the body in the proper place. Some groups of invertebrate ancestors to the vertebrates have one set of Hox genes. Then as the vertebrates evolved, the Hox genes were duplicated a couple of times, so most vertebrates have four sets. A further duplication of three of these sets happened in some fish. So we see that evolution provided the extra Hox genes for animals with more complex structures and more variability that needed the more sophisticated control of embryology. This is clear evidence for evolution.

I will give just one more example, and that should be enough to clinch the case for evolution. All living organisms have the same biochemical system in their cells. This shows that they all evolved from the same ancestor, and the biochemical system evolved only once. Otherwise, different animals would be expected to have different biochemical systems.

CARL. You're right that these are examples of a huge category of evidence always used to prove evolution. I am not sure I could explain all of them, but your illustrations and others like them don't demonstrate what you think they do—not at all.

For example, two possible explanations exist for the common biochemistry of all organisms. If life evolved, then your explanation would be correct: all life came from one common ancestor. But if life was created, then the evidence says the Creator designed one biochemical system and used that in all life-forms. That is all that we can conclude from this type of evidence. It can't tell us whether life evolved or was created. That decision comes from those all-important assumptions we all make.

The same is true for the fascinating Hox genes. Did evolution duplicate them, or did the Creator give each animal group the number of Hox genes they needed, according to their level of complexity? Each answer is based on a required assumption.

Where the assumptions meet the evidence is at the point where we analyze the details of biochemistry and the genetic-epigenetic system. Then the awesome complexity and sophistication of it all eliminates, I believe, the possibility that such overwhelming intricacy and precision could develop through random mutations and natural selection.

ED. I don't know about all of this. As I said before, I also have questions I can't answer. I will have to stay with the scientific method, however, which cannot accept any type of supernatural or even any type of genetic or epigenetic foresight that can know what will be good for an animal. It all must begin with Darwin's random variation.

CARL. We are back where we began. We can't demonstrate or prove how life arose and developed. We all have unanswered questions, and we each make a choice of what assumptions to start with.

One other perspective exists that we can't ignore. You have a lot of confidence that the evolutionary biologists who study nature, speaking here of evolutionary history, understand it all better than the molecular biologists in their laboratories. There's a very basic flaw in that logic. The molecular biologists, studying the molecular processes that underlie evolution, are dealing with what is happening right in front of them, minute by minute, in living organisms. Even though the complexity of life makes their research challenging, they can keep collecting evidence on these active, continuous processes that are happening *right now*.

In contrast, the study of evolutionary history is attempting to figure out events that happened, or are presumed to have happened, in the distant past and cannot be observed by us. Since we can't observe these events, we have a big handicap in trying to determine what actually did happen.

ED. I see what you're saying, but that is where those fossils become important, and you haven't explained them.

CARL. True, and on the other side there are orphan genes, the demise of junk DNA, and a number of other challenging issues yet to be explained by any naturalistic theory of evolution. I guess we will need to continue this tomorrow.

ED. I suppose. This could be endless! Another nagging question about your God is this: How can you say He is a loving God who values our freedom of choice? How can that be, since your God still demands that we accept His dominating power? If we don't, we will die instead of having eternal life.

CARL. Imagine with me for a moment that there might be a different reason why only some people will live forever. Maybe God gives eternal life only to those who would enjoy it. Does that sound weird? Is it possible that some people would not enjoy life in a universe where everybody is kind and unselfish, and no one is interested in dominating or controlling anyone else?

ED. Interesting idea. I hadn't thought of that. Hmm. It can't be true, but if it was, it would make God look very different from what many of us think. Tomorrow, let's stay with the science. That is where the real issues lie.

CHAPTER 9

Macroevolution Once More

ED. All this business about doubting biological evolution makes me think that more discussion of those rocks would be better than this topic! But you still have some problems to solve before I let you off the hook on macroevolution. For example—the fossils.

CARL. If you remember what Darwin said about fossils, that's a good place to start. He knew that the fossil record didn't contain the innumerable evolutionary intermediate forms that would show that evolution of one group from another actually happened. His discussion of fossils focused on explaining why he thought the fossil record did not support his theory. He thought that after a lot more searching was done we would find many of those intermediate forms.

But the major transitional forms haven't been found. Essentially, no convincing evolutionary intermediates between phyla or most classes of organisms have been found. Another problem with the fossil record is that the earliest fossils are different from those that come later in the record, but they are not actually simple. The same amazing biochemistry we see in living organisms now was there from the beginning. The early trilobites, for example, had the same complex legs, bodies, and sophisticated compound eyes as living arthropods do now. So I'm not sure why you think the fossils will show that my thinking is wrong.

ED. Certainly you are aware of the fossil *Tiktaalik*, the perfect intermediate between fish and tetrapods, the four-footed vertebrates; or of the Triassic fossils that show various intermediate forms of the mammal ear bones that evolved from reptile jawbones. As you look farther up in the Triassic rocks, these fossils gradually look more and more like mammals. Or what about the feathered dinosaurs that demonstrate the evolution of birds from dinosaurs?

CARL. Those are famous examples, but do they show what you think they show? I'll begin with the most difficult one first. Those Triassic fossils that seem to have changing ear and jaw bones are the most puzzling to me. They are a strange and complex phenomenon, but still not the type of evidence needed to decide whether mammals evolved from reptiles.

I'll suggest one very preliminary possibility. It looks as though a set of genes, under the control of epigenetic or other DNA management systems, can be used to make the extra jawbones in reptiles, or mammal ear bones, and the Creator designed them that way. Perhaps in the Triassic a variety of species had damaging mutations of this system, resulting in those puzzling fossils. This explanation does not explain all the complexities of these fossils, even for me. It will not be acceptable to most scientists, and I don't suppose it will convince you. But my purpose is to begin to understand what the options could be for a creationist like myself.

ED. Nice try, but I am not convinced. Now how about the others?

CARL. OK, now the origin of land-dwelling vertebrates. The discovery of *Tiktaalik* is an interesting case of a successful research result coming from a bad theory. A group of paleontologists wanted to find the transitional form from fish to tetrapods, so they examined the rocks of the right age, of the right paleoenvironment, and in the right geographic location. Success! They found a fossil with the almost perfect transitional anatomy—*Tiktaalik*.

Then a few years later, a paper was published describing good fossil tetrapod tracks in Poland, and according to radiometric dates they're twelve million years older than *Tiktaalik*. What does that mean? Even though *Tiktaalik* has the anatomical features that seem right for the intermediate, it can't be the ancestor of tetrapods, because tetrapods lived long before it existed. Now radiometric dating is causing problems for *your* theory! Also, creationists can suggest other good reasons why *Tiktaalik* was designed with those anatomical features.

These paleontologists looking for tetrapod ancestors used some good information to hypothesize where to find the intermediate. They found what they were looking for, but their hypothesis was dead wrong! There must be another reason, other than an evolutionary sequence, for why those fossils are buried in the order they are.

The feathered dinosaurs are more interesting, but they say more about the role of hypotheses and assumptions than about evolution. If a person has chosen to believe that birds resulted from evolution, rather than creation, they will simply be asking which group of animals are the most likely ancestors of birds. In that case, the dinosaurs appear to be the best option for a bird ancestor. But if you don't make the assumption of evolution, and ask whether birds evolved or were created, it's a very different situation.

First of all, a long discussion has been going on about whether some dinosaurs were warm-blooded. If they were, they would need some type of insulation, and if so, why not feathers? Is there a good reason to think the Creator would not give some dinosaurs feathers? Reptiles are more anatomically similar to birds than to mammals, so probably feathers would be a more logical choice for dinosaur insulation than hair or fur.

A considerable variety of feathered dinosaurs and Mesozoic birds has been found, and their limb skeletons are similar. The bigger question is whether this is evidence for the evolution of flight, or if there was just a variety of flying birds and nonflying feathered dinosaurs. Having feathers doesn't show that these dinosaurs were on the way to flight, and there is no definite evidence for how dinosaurs would actually begin to fly. No convincing fossil evidence for the evolution of flight in birds has been discovered, and the situation is even worse for bats or pterosaurs, the flying reptiles.

ED. But most scientists know that these flying creatures evolved from nonflying animals. I suppose you will claim that this belief is only the result of the assumption that there is no creator. Do you really think evolutionists are so shallow?

CARL. I don't think they are shallow, but I can't agree with their logic or their conclusions. If the fossil or other scientific evidence for the evolution of flight is not convincing, what am I supposed to think is behind their belief in the evolution of flight? Since the evidence is missing, what alternative is there to my interpretation that the belief in evolution of flight is only an assumption—the assumption of naturalism?

ED. OK, I will have to agree that we all make assumptions. But some assumptions you have to make if you want others to accept you as a real scientist.

CARL. By "some assumptions," you really mean one particular assumption—the assumption that there is no creator, or if there is a Creator, he or she or it hasn't done anything that would affect science. In other words, the assumption that all animals came to be by the laws of chemistry and physics alone, with no intelligent help.

ED. You finally got it!

CARL. Well, you can put me in whatever category you wish, but I am more interested in seeking truth than in being accepted into a particular club of scientists. And a few things about macroevolution still need to be out on the table.

If life is all the result of evolution, with no creator or other intelligent designer, then every gene that exists must have evolved in short steps from other similar genes in ancestors. That was a comfortable interpretation for scientists to hold before our new ability to sequence the genomes of many organisms. Now we know that many orphan genes have no precursor genes in any ancestral group. These genes just appear, with no ancestors! And there are thousands of them, seemingly in all groups of organisms. Humans have at least a thousand orphan genes. This is a serious problem for macroevolution—maybe even an overwhelming, unsolvable problem.

ED. If that were real, it would be a big problem, but we will wait and see what new evidence appears that will modify this situation. Evolution-based science will win this argument in the end.

CARL. That's fair enough. That is often the best response for all of us: don't get too concerned while we wait to see what new discoveries science has to offer. A lot of research is being done on this, however, and the orphan gene problem keeps getting worse for evolution, not better.

I will mention just one more biological problem. For years the bulk of our DNA was interpreted as junk DNA—leftover junk from the evolution process. This junk DNA also had one important function in evolution. It was the proposed source of unused genes that could evolve into new genes with a new function. But increasing evidence shows that at least part of this "junk" actually had an important function, and in 2012 the results of the massive ENCODE research project pretty well eliminated the old "junk DNA" idea. The new evidence indicates that the supposed junk DNA is functional, with often quite important functions. In this case, waiting for more evidence really did help us gain a better understanding of whether evolution or design gives the best explanation.

ED. I think we will not agree as to which explanation is true. But don't change the subject! We are getting away from the fossils, and more questions remain.

CARL. I agree, and I'm not done with the fossils. We need to talk about at least three last bits of fossil evidence. Stephen Gould was one of the authors of the theory of punctuated equilibrium, the theory that evolution occurs in short spurts, and because the changes happen rapidly they don't leave fossil evidence. The reason why Gould and Niles Eldredge developed that theory is that Gould was bothered by the lack of visible evidence for evolutionary change in the fossils. Typically, a fossil species appears in the record, changes very little over time, or more likely not at all, then disappears from the fossil record and is replaced by other species. This is not an occasional problem but is the normal pattern with fossils. Is Gould's theory an adequate solution to the problem?

ED. I was not a fan of Stephen Gould and his questionable ideas. But his theory was a better solution than relying on some doubtful creator to invent all these fossil species, let them die and disappear, then make more species to replace them! What kind of a God would that be? Gould's theory was at least a realistic scientific theory, whether or not it was a sufficient theory.

CARL. He did follow the proper assumptions that you wish for us to rely on. But his theory claimed that all those intermediates between species would just *happen* to rarely be preserved as fossils. If it all worked the way he suggested, his theory asks me to believe that almost all those intermediates would escape being preserved, and just about the only fossils were the ones that were not evolving. The fossilization process somehow selected the nonevolving ones to preserve! It could happen that way sometimes—but almost always? That is asking me to believe way too much in very improbable events.

ED. Those are challenging issues for me as well, but we haven't yet addressed one of the biggest problems for your Bible-based theory. The vertebrate fossils form a clear evolutionary sequence. Fish come first in the rocks. Then as we go up through time we find amphibians, then reptiles, then birds and mammals, in the order of their evolution. And many of the most highly evolved vertebrate groups that are still living today didn't evolve until later—in the upper part of the Cenozoic. How are you going to wiggle out of that compelling evidence for evolution?

CARL. That is one of the more difficult issues for us, and I don't have a completely satisfying explanation for you. We suggest that aquatic animals would be expected to get killed and buried first in a big flood, but that is only a partial explanation. But I can give you a straightforward answer that I believe makes the fossil sequence far from compelling. You remember our discussion of the discoveries of modern molecular biology that are destroying the credibility of macroevolution? Since a viable process for evolving new classes of animals doesn't seem to exist, there must be a different reason, other than evolution, for the sequence of fossil vertebrates.

ED. If you really were right about those molecular biologists, I could see your logic. But since looking at all of the evidence tells us that the animal world is the result of evolution, I am not sure your excuse is adequate. Don't blame it all on our assumptions! The vertebrate sequence can't be so easily brushed aside.

CARL. We are still on different sides of the philosophical divide. And we both have difficult problems to deal with. I don't really understand the vertebrate fossil sequence either. But before we go away from fossils, here is another of those tough problems for you to solve. As Darwin and other evolutionists like yourself view history, life began in the dim past, and random changes gradually varied organisms as they evolved new features of anatomy or physiology. It would take a very long sequence of small variations before a new body type would be ready—like a new class or phylum. The fossil record should show this pattern—the early fossils should include many new species or genera, but only gradually, later, would new phyla, new body plans, appear in the record.

But that is not the way it is! Most of the phyla that occur as fossils appear suddenly at the base of the Cambrian—the "Cambrian explosion"—and then more variation within these phyla gradually appears in the rest of the fossil record. The big evolutionary events—the invention of many phyla—happened first, and small variations came later. It almost looks as though evolution got it backward, even impossibly backward!

ED. Do you think you have all the answers? That is an interesting puzzle, but we were not there to see how it happened, so how should we know how to explain everything? At least my answers to the tough questions don't ask me to believe in magic.

CARL. I am not enjoying pushing this too far, but forgive me for a final summary comment. As we discussed earlier, we agreed that small-scale evolutionary changes like new species and genera are supported by abundant evidence. But I truly believe that is where the good news for evolution stops. For reasons we have talked about, and quite a few more, I think the probability of macroevolution occurring is very low to nonexistent. Think of the new molecular inventions needed to go from laying eggs to bearing live young, or to change a reptile brain into a human brain, or to become fully warm-blooded, with all its physiological implications, or to invent the wonderful vertebrate skeleton. And that is only the beginning! The huge bulk of the evidence is dramatically against that ever happening. That theory of macroevolution seemed feasible in the mid-1800s, when scientists knew very little about the awesome complexity of living things. But now? Even though many scientists reject the idea of a wise, all-knowing Creator, without Him they are stuck in the mire left over from Darwin's naive idea.

ED. It is very clear where you stand on this matter. I feel sorry for you, but it isn't likely I can change your mind. And your arguments won't change my views on evolution. You raise some legitimate and challenging questions, but your approach doesn't include the creativity to search for answers that don't require a mythical God to intervene.

I have another concern. You won't accept the possibility that maybe there has to be a naturalistic mechanism, like macroevolution, to produce the life-forms. You won't even allow that to be on an equal standing with your ideas of creation. So why do you think you are more open-minded than I am?

CARL. I suggest that my confidence in God makes it easier for me to candidly examine both options, but it would actually be difficult to demonstrate which of us is more open-minded. Neither of us can demonstrate the truth of our thinking about origins. This has more to do with the assumptions we accept, and those assumptions have a strong bearing on what evidence we think is most important and most reliable, and even worth taking seriously. After all of our conversations, I can't say you don't know enough about my views to evaluate them. Our assumptions and philosophical choices just seem to lead us in different directions.

ED. I have to reluctantly agree with you that we each make assumptions that have a strong influence on the types of explanations and theories we accept. The assumptions add up to what is often called a worldview, and my worldview doesn't lead me into the pit of thinking that some deity can snap his fingers and make animals appear out of thin air.

CARL. That possibility is hard for us humans to comprehend, but if there is no God, then where did matter and energy come from? Where did the exquisite set of physical and chemical laws come from? The laws that are so finely tuned? Did they just appear by themselves?

You could ask me where God came from, and I could not answer. Our inability to explain the origin of the laws of chemistry and physics doesn't mean those laws don't exist, and it does not mean God doesn't exist. The reality is that, no matter what we think the answers are to these puzzles of origins, as *we* look back in the chain of causation, all finite humans come to a point where we have *no answers*.

If God does exist, however, then the next steps in the chain of causation, for origins, are believable. If there were no God, they would be impossible.

ED. OK, we may never agree on this, but tomorrow let's go back to geology and radiometric dating. I will pin you to the wall!

CHAPTER 10

The Eternal Rocks?

ED. That was just an average breakfast this morning! But I feel ready to challenge your assumptions again. I suppose you prayed for good answers to stump me today. We will see. Did you fill the gasoline tank?

CARL. I did fill it. That's one puzzle I don't want to try to answer—where to get more gasoline out in the wilderness!

ED. The other day you showed me some amazing rock formations covering huge pieces of real estate. That is a puzzle, but a lot of ancient geological history is weird, so what is new? If you want to make the Morrison Formation a catastrophic deposit formed in months or a few years instead of millions of years you are up against the radiometric dates, and that is pure, no-nonsense physics. The sequence of elements and how each decays to the next step in the sequence is straightforward physics. How does your Bible deal with that?

CARL. Of course, the Bible leaves questions like that up to us to study out. I guess the Creator knows that if we had all the answers we would get much too arrogant! I will give you the best answers I can, but I still prefer not to do it in a way that would ruin our friendship.

Now to deal with the no-nonsense physics. You're right that the decay of the unstable ions in radioactive elements is pretty well understood physics. The physicist in the dating lab takes a rock sample and analyzes the pertinent elements in the sample. The physicist determines the amount of each element, applies some necessary interpretation, and calculates the age of the sample. Of course, no possible instrument exists that can directly determine the age of the rock in years. The instruments determine the ratio of parent-to-daughter isotopes; that is what is measured, except for carbon 14, in which case the number of disintegrations per unit time is measured. The researcher then must make some assumptions and calculate the actual age. Sorry, but there are assumptions even in the dating laboratory.

Ed. I suppose you think that God might have monkeyed with the physics! Is that the assumption you make?

Carl. I don't assume that, and I don't know any reason why He would deliberately do so. But if God did interject some force into earth's structure that resulted in a catastrophic global flood—as an emergency measure, to deal with all the human and animal violence that was destroying His plan for mankind—I suppose that side effects could have influenced the radioactive elements. That is not the main point I wish to make, however. What happens in the dating laboratory may be good physics, but even if we leave God out of the picture, that is not the whole story. Not even close. Before a rock sample reaches the laboratory for dating, that sample had a long history, and there are limits to how well we can know that history and how it affected the physical makeup of the sample.

Let's say this dating process is used on volcanic material, or some other rock that was molten and came to the surface. The time we want to know is the time since it formed the layer we sampled, not some event earlier in its history. What were those earlier conditions? What if, as some believe, time passed between the creation of the universe and the creation of life on earth? What if our sample had mixed or otherwise interacted with other magma? If we have any uncertainties about how to interpret the date we calculate, we have reason to take seriously the other geological evidence that conflicts with the radiometric dates. And we find a lot of that conflicting evidence—not just a few odd things. I'm afraid it's not "solid, certain physics" versus fuzzy geology. We can know more about how sediments form, processes we can observe today, than we can know about radiometric events from the distant past, not observable by us.

Ed. Now you really are inserting your God, meddling with history! I don't like that, and I am still skeptical, so convince me. It is true that we can't observe the distant past, but the rock formations are in a sequence, one above the other, and the radiometric dates for those rocks are in the correct order.

CARL. In general they are, but some incidents raise doubts, for me, that radiometric dating is so solid. Human knowledge about the ancient past is not nearly adequate to support the level of assurance about radioisotope dating that you express. And bear with me as I talk through this for a while. What if God is real, and He did involve Himself in history? Do we want to know that, or to pretend it isn't so? More evidence emerges to reckon with that doesn't fit the conventional geological theory.

We saw some formations that are spread over a huge geographic area, the Morrison and Shinarump formations. Those are just the proverbial tip of the iceberg. Many more such formations exist, and to fully understand the rock record we must look beyond individual formations. Sure, it is necessary, for accurate geological description, to assess and name individual formations, since the outer geographic limits of a formation may be covered by other rocks and not be observable. Also, we often can't determine the nature of covered deposits in the intervening area between one formation and the next deposit of the same age. But unfortunately, all these individual formation names can obscure the larger picture. If only we could take a photograph of North America, for example, with a camera that made younger rocks disappear and only showed Permian rocks approximately equivalent in age to the Coconino Sandstone. We would see that equivalent sandstone formations lie to the east and north, and the Coconino is a part of a vast sand sea covering much of the western United States. How did that enormous sand sea get there without the underlying canyons and hills so typical of our modern world? And this one instance is only the beginning.

Some geologists have looked at this concept continent-wide, or even at the global picture, and even though they are not creationists they have revealed some very helpful insights. In the Grand Canyon is a Mississippian limestone, the Redwall Limestone. It has characteristics that appear in Mississippian limestones in the Appalachian Mountains of eastern North America and across the Midwest. Mississippian limestones in the Canadian Rockies and in Alaska are recognizable by their fossils as part of this same geological episode. And that is not all! Equivalent limestones appear across western Europe and the British Isles, and into part of Asia and western

Australia. Other limestones are present in other parts of the geological column, but limestones are not all the same. These Mississippian limestones are recognizable as the same deposit that appears at many places around the globe.

Many have heard of the white cliffs of Dover, on the British coast, made of chalk. These are thick deposits of quite pure coccolith limestones—the skeletons of minute organisms—with pieces of black flint and a set of characteristic fossils. This Upper Cretaceous deposit, with the same characteristics, and with almost no good equivalent in other parts of the geological column, occurs with an amazingly wide distribution. It is found along the Black Sea, in France and Germany, across Scandinavia, Ireland, Poland, Bulgaria, Georgia, Egypt, and Israel. Furthermore, an essentially identical Upper Cretaceous deposit occurs across the southern United States and in western Australia. If this was not part of a significant global geological event, then why is this type of chalk deposit found almost exclusively in the Upper Cretaceous, and worldwide?

In the Triassic are characteristic red deposits of sandstone, shale, and mudstone. They are often composed of three formations, with a set of features that can be easily recognized by experienced field geologists as "Triassic red beds." They are well represented in western North America, Germany, Spain, Bulgaria, Morocco, the eastern United States, southwestern United States, Mexico, and China.

At a conference, a geologist from Argentina saw photos from China and quickly identified the rocks as Triassic red beds. Why are these characteristic red deposits all over the world in the Triassic? Why would not similar environments, producing such similar types of "red beds," not be found in various places, at different times in geological history?

Abundant coal deposits in the Pennsylvanian period and in the Cretaceous to Paleocene are quite different from one another. The familiar and abundant Pennsylvanian coals are widely distributed in the eastern United States, Texas, Britain, and from Ireland to the north of the Caspian Sea in Asia. Why are they so widespread, and why is this type of coal in just one part of geological history? And these examples are just the beginning.

ED. I am skeptical of all those examples. What is your source for those?

Creation? Really?

Did you see all of those rock formations?

CARL. That information is primarily from the reputable British geologist Derek Ager. During his career he deliberately traveled worldwide to become personally acquainted with global geology and recognized the global nature of many of these deposits. In his book he talked only about geological evidence he had personally seen, so these features could be even more widespread in the world. He warned creationists not to use his evidence to support their theories! Why did he feel it necessary to make that statement? He understood that the evidence he described was puzzling for his deep-time worldview, and he didn't want anyone to think he was a creationist or Bible believer. As you can see, I don't think his warning was justified; his evidence is more compatible with my understanding of earth history than with his.

ED. All you are saying is that similar rocks formed in many parts of the world at specific times. Why is that a problem for deep time? It seems logical that one stage in earth history might result in similar deposits in different places.

CARL. Perhaps that is to be expected at times, but when it happens too often it needs a specific explanation. This is true even if, in some of these episodes, we see some shifting in time from place to place, but still close together in time. There is something global about the general sequence of sedimentary deposits that we see in the geological column, and it's doubtful that this could be an expected outcome of processes similar to those we observe on earth today. It seems that geological deposits in Australia should be controlled primarily by circumstances in Australia, rather than synchronized with those in Europe, for example. We're seeing too much global synchrony in what was being deposited at each stage in history.

I suggest that the global nature of such deposits is more readily explained if a rapid global geological event produced a sequence of types of deposits, and the sequence occurs simultaneously at many places globally to produce the record we see in the rocks. That suggestion will not be taken seriously by many scientists, because they will not accept the ancient story of a global geological event.

Ed. Of course not! You are bringing religion into science again.

Carl. The difference in our thinking is again the result of our different assumptions. Right? *Where* I got my idea is irrelevant. If your objection is to be evidence-based, science-based, then it must go beyond grumbling about my religion. You need to give physical evidence to refute my suggestions. Do you have a better geological explanation than mine?

Ed. The evidence you cite does seems to indicate, as you say, surprising global synchrony in geological processes. Standard geological theory perhaps would not have predicted such a peculiar thing, but our task is to find standard geological answers that depend only on the laws of nature.

Carl. That's what I would expect you to say, and I wish you success in finding such an answer. But there's more. If this global nature of geological deposits was the only problem for conventional geology, you might have a point. But there is much more, and the global nature of the record is only part of this even larger picture.

Remember that in conventional geology, the entire geological past is to be explained by processes observable or feasible in the modern world. We see today how rivers carve their channels and deposit sediments. We see sediment being deposited in various bodies of water and then the sediment is churned up by living animals that burrow through the sediment, a process called bioturbation, destroying evidence of discrete layers of mud or sand. Much of the sedimentary record was formed in water, and this destruction of boundaries between sediment layers should be the normal process. Even on a floodplain that doesn't necessarily remain under water, plant roots, worms, and mouse burrows do their part to destroy the organized, recognizable layers of sediment.

Then why, in so many sedimentary rocks, do we see clear layers of sediment whose boundaries have not been destroyed by animal activity or plant roots?

Ed. I object. Scientists have found plenty of fossil animal burrows or tracks, and even some plant roots, and that refute your argument!

Carl. You are right to say those things do exist in some rocks, but it is uncommon to find rocks with enough of this type of disturbance to destroy or even obscure the distinct rock layers or beds. The rock record is full of clearly bedded rocks, well enough preserved for geologists to find lots of evidence on which to base interpretations of specific geological processes. And creationists are not the only ones who wonder why there is not more bioturbation in the rocks. I am not talking about occasional distinct bedding. *This is normally the way it is.* Why? This looks like the result of a rapid global geological event, not slow deposits over deep time.

Also, we don't find the amount of erosion at each interval of geological history that we see in our modern world. Remember the rock layers we saw at the Grand Canyon. Those even layers stretched as far as we could see, without hills, valleys, or canyons cut into each layer before the next formation was deposited on top of it. And those even, relatively uneroded layers went much farther than we could see from the canyon rim. That is generally characteristic of the Paleozoic and the Mesozoic.

And there's more. Compared with rates of sediment deposition on earth today, we see only a fraction of the sedimentary rock necessary to account for 541 million years since early Cambrian.

ED. You have raised at least two different issues. The first, the abundance of bedded rocks in which the bedding was not destroyed by bioturbation, is another of those geological oddities that the conventional model would not have predicted, but it happened, for some unknown reason.

The second issue is the shortage of sediments. That is not a secret. The geological community is aware of this, and they have an explanation that seems quite good to me. The explanation is that only the occasional deposit gets preserved; the rest get eroded away after deposition and are not preserved. A position in the rocks that shows evidence of erosional removal of sediment is called an unconformity. There are many known unconformities in the record. So what is the problem?

CARL. Those unconformities do exist, but the problem is this: the conclusion that only a small percentage of the expected sediment was preserved is calculated *after the known, recognizable unconformities are accounted for.* Think about what that means. It means that most of the hypothesized erosional unconformities are just that—a hypothesis. They are required by the theory but are not supported by evidence. I prefer to go by the evidence, and the evidence does not indicate nearly enough sediment to account for the deep time, or nearly enough erosion to explain the lack of sediment.

ED. That's an intriguing point that you raise. I don't know how to answer it. I will have to think about it. The geological record has many odd features; that is not news to those of us who use only science, not magic, to interpret what we see in the earth. Your mistake is your choice to make an issue of these oddities and ignore the clear evidence of the radiometric dates. If the dates indicate deep time, then that is reality, and we just don't know enough yet to explain the features you are overemphasizing.

CARL. I understand your objection, but I doubt its validity. You have to hold on to the radiometric timescale and doubt the significance of my other evidence, because it could destroy your worldview. Since there is so much evidence that is problematic for deep time, and for other aspects of conventional geological theory, that should be taken seriously. If the radiometric timescale is correct, why is there so much evidence that goes so strongly against it?

The nature of the erosion that shapes the landscape has dramatically changed through time. In the later part of geological history the earth has been carved into the scenery we enjoy exploring today, with its dramatic canyons, mountains, high cliffs, and winding slot canyons. It was not always so. The Paleozoic and Mesozoic rock formations, before modern erosion, are remarkably flat, unbroken by deep canyons and cliffs. That doesn't mean no erosion. There were episodes of erosion; there were even some canyons. It is not surprising that a catastrophe would result in erosion. The surprise is that there is so little of this in comparison to what we see happening in our modern world. Something was strikingly different in those earlier times. While sediments were being deposited on a global scale, it was not subject to the degree of dramatic erosion that came later, after the catastrophe.

One more feature of the lack of sediment is quite interesting.

It is sometimes stated that there is so much "missing sediment," because the sedimentary record preserves only what results from catastrophes—storms or other exceptional events that destroy other sediments and leave their own deposits there to be preserved. If this is valid, that is what I would expect—much of the geological record is the result of catastrophic events. But where, in the rocks, is the evidence of all the supposed vast time between catastrophic events? Perhaps it was primarily one long catastrophe.

Ed. You've got me cornered with that one! But not for long. You accuse me of relying on assumptions, but your interpretation still flies in the face of the radiometric timescale. You don't take that evidence seriously but allow your religious assumptions to raise all these doubts about curiosities that real geologists don't see as a problem.

Carl. Are they really just curiosities? Or are they awesome challenges that others don't notice, because their worldview doesn't give them reason to notice them or take them seriously? Do you think the things I have been telling you are not correct?

Ed. No, I don't have reasons to doubt the truth of the evidence you present. But the conclusions you draw from the evidence just don't fit with what thousands of very good scientists are saying. How could you think you know better?

Carl. It isn't a matter of knowing better or being smarter. But the best choice isn't always the one that the majority prefers. Sometimes it is risky to be too tied to the majority opinions; like for a person in 1955 who believed the then-unconventional idea that continents could move around. That is especially true if the Creator of the universe disagrees with the majority. Maybe we should take the hint.

Ed. That old book again!

Carl. The majority should not be too readily ignored, but in dealing with events of the distant past that we can't observe, and especially if we have troublesome evidence, if the majority is too firmly in agreement, their unanimity can seem a bit too good to be true. Do we know enough about the ancient past to be that sure of our interpretations? Something besides the evidence is governing their thinking.

ED. Now let me bring in another line of reasoning. What if there is a God, even one that meddled with earth history, but He just didn't do it in the literal way that you think the Bible says? I don't think that is a worthwhile perspective, but if it were true, what would that do to your reasoning?

CARL. A very good question, especially because that is the approach that many Christians take. They want to fit science and faith together in a way that doesn't require them to question prevailing scientific opinion. They typically propose that God was in some way involved in history and origins, but He "created" through the evolution process over millions of years. They call it theistic evolution or something similar. Is that what you're referring to?

ED. Yes, basically. I notice that this is a common interpretation.

CARL. To evaluate that approach, we should ask several questions. For one, is it true to the accepted scientific method? Second, is it compatible with the message of the Bible? Furthermore, how does it compare with the scientific evidence?

On the first question I will have to agree with Jerry Coyne and others. Bringing God into the origins process negates the standard scientific method, no matter how subtly we try to sneak Him into the process.

The second question is more complex, but I will argue that creation by evolution through deep time refutes the Bible's primary theme. This theme is that humans were created sinless, in the Garden of Eden; then they fell into sin, which is why Jesus died—to redeem humankind from their fallen state. In the Bible, humans and relationships are of ultimate value to God, and salvation from sin is real. If humans resulted from evolution, then no Garden of Eden was created and no Fall happened. It also means that God is responsible for the evil, death, and suffering in the world, because according to this view, evolution was initiated by God as His means of creating. If so, then what is the purpose of Jesus' death? And what does redemption mean? This negates the entire Christian message.

My answer to the third question may surprise you, but it probably shouldn't, after all of our discussions. Although scientific evidence has come into view that I don't know how to explain, you also have much evidence that is incompatible with your worldview. I will suggest that current evidence is refuting Darwin's theory of evolution by random mutations and natural selection. Perhaps it is more important that a lot of geological evidence I have presented, plus those ancient biochemicals, are not compatible with deep time and conventional geological theory. In summary, I suggest that concepts like theistic evolution are incompatible with both the Bible and modern scientific evidence. For me, the theological problems are the final, determining ones.

I also still see something besides the evidence, something having more to do with philosophy and assumptions being the deciding factor for persons on all sides of this issue. This is largely a philosophical choice, not a scientific choice.

ED. Perhaps so, and I guess I do have more objections to your philosophy than to your evidence. But it may not be worth risking your reputation as a scientist to move away from the accepted interpretations of science.

CARL. Is it improper to think independently and question prevailing opinion? If all scientists had always been so concerned about agreeing with the majority, we would still be teaching our students that the sun rotates around the earth. Wisdom has its place, even if it suggests an unpopular conclusion.

Tomorrow is the last day of our trip. So tomorrow I might as well be brave and tell you just how I put it all together.

ED. Thanks for the warning. I'd better get good sleep tonight!

CHAPTER 11

A Synthesis

ED. OK, I am ready for the synthesis you have to present. I can deal with the indigestion when I get home tonight!

CARL. I don't have the final word for you, but one scenario in geological history has more meaning than is normally recognized. The geological record reveals a master sequence of environmental situations and processes rather than a random variation on the modern world through time. The sequence I will summarize is documented in the rocks and thus is a valid sequence of events, whether or not you are willing to see its proposed relation to a global flood, as I interpret it.

The story begins sometime after the Creation week, with the Cambrian explosion, when most phyla of animals appeared suddenly. This was at the beginning of the global flood and was followed by a Paleozoic time period with an awful lot of rocks formed in a marine world. An awesome amount of limestone formed during this time. Note that very little limestone, in comparison, is forming today. The evidence implies that most or all of the continents were under shallow oceans during that time. In the later part of this time, still in the Paleozoic, came the globally distributed limestone equivalents of the Redwall Limestone.

Also, as the mountains in eastern North America rose up in the last half of the Paleozoic, an enormous amount of plant material settled into mats that became the Carboniferous coal, with a distribution that also spans the globe. Something killed a lot of plants to make this coal. Basically all during the Paleozoic and Mesozoic the rock formations still exhibit the geographically widespread nature we visited in western North America. Something with a global character was underway all during this time. After the Paleozoic period, deposits were made from terrestrial environments, along with some that was still marine.

The Cenozoic brought increasing differences in the rocks and the types of life abundantly preserved as fossils. Early Cenozoic may be the time when the terrestrial animals preserved through the major flood catastrophe again spread over the earth. It is probable that during and after the Flood an unimaginable amount of trees and other plant debris floated on the ocean surface, facilitating the movements of animals and plants around the world. The animals and plants adapted to their new environmental situations as the oceans increasingly receded from the continents, and a great number of new species appeared as small-scale evolution adapted them to their changed world. These adaptations occurred, I propose, within the genetic potential placed in each group by the Creator.

At this time, Cretaceous into early Cenozoic, the Cretaceous and Paleocene coal accumulated, and the Rocky Mountains in western North America formed and changed the landscape. Geological formations after this were more localized rather than widespread over hundreds of thousands of square miles. The earth in the Cenozoic gradually came to more closely resemble the world we know, with successively less of the land being underwater. The evidence just happens to fit my theory. Large lakes were left over as the oceans receded from the continents, and these lakes finally dried up as well. Examples of these were the Eocene lakes that resulted in the Green River Formation in Wyoming and nearby states.

The continents continued to move—rapidly, I believe—as they also did before the Cenozoic. Then their movement slowed to the current snail's pace. In the late Cenozoic, continuing to the present time, sedimentary deposits became even more localized. Some geological phenomena still had a global character, especially those dependent on environmental changes as the earth adjusted after the Flood. An example is the massive blooms of diatoms in late Miocene and early Pliocene that produced deposits of diatomite in many places, with their beautifully preserved fossils, from insects to whales, testifying to the rapid processes occurring.

Finally, during the Pleistocene, sedimentary deposits were even more progressively localized. An example of this can be observed in Death Valley, California, in tufa deposits that, during the Pleistocene, began as several square miles in area, then reduced by at least

50 to 70 percent. Today only a small spring remains, still depositing the same tufa on the plants and rocks. Climatic changes came, perhaps also an aftermath of the global geological catastrophe. This included the Ice Age, with ice covering the northern parts of North America and Europe. Later still, some other climate swings came along, such as the Little Ice Age in Europe, from about A.D. 1450 to 1850.

During this geological adventure lasting thousands of years, the earth progressively changed, until finally, gradually settling down to a more stable condition. We still experience the remnants of this Cambrian to Pleistocene global geological sequence in earthquakes, storms, volcanoes, and landslides.

The history we reviewed began with those very large-scale geological processes during the first two-thirds or so of that history, then narrowed to more and more localized events, with the early evidence of global oceans changing the earth to as it is now.

Most of what I have described has strong evidence for it. Other proposed geological events or processes, I think, are not supported by adequate evidence, such as a Paleozoic ice age, and the Milankovitch climatic cycles. Much more is not included in this brief survey—enough to keep us studying and thinking for a good many years.

ED. That is wild! I guess you are serious about this, despite the radiometric data. The scenario you present does explain a lot of evidence, but it still requires your God to meddle with history. This boggles my mind, but I understand your thinking a little better.

CARL. The radiometric timescale, partly physics and partly geological history, cannot be just written off. It is important, but it doesn't necessarily have the last word. So many things in geology don't fit the timescale or other parts of the conventional geology explanatory system; there has to be a hitch in there somewhere. A geologist friend of mine is skeptical of traditional Flood geology but also says that "conventional geology doesn't work either. There must be a third way." I suggest the third way can be described as a more careful approach to Flood geology, based on as much evidence as can be put together, plus, probably, a lot more that will be based on future research. I wish you would see fit to take another look at explanations for origins and consider various options.

ED. You and I will never agree on these things, but I still have enjoyed this trip—sometimes tiresome but never boring. You are a nice guy, and perhaps that is the one useful result of your religion.

CARL. I am glad you at least see me that way. But before we finish our discussion I would like to challenge your thinking even a little more.

ED. OK, go ahead. I am ready for anything!

CARL. You and many others think we are being foolish to take the Bible seriously and let it influence our scientific thinking. I propose to you a very different perspective: I propose that naturalistic thinking, and the resulting worldview of millions of years of evolution, has turned science into a very wrong and even a dead-end road. The scientists who follow this road are still fairly successful, partly because they all agree on this worldview and all use it to interpret their data. This brings a measure of uniformity to their thinking.

I have tried to show you that new evidence often brings challenges to their explanations. For example, the ancient proteins in fossils, the global synchrony in geological deposits, the molecular biology challenges to macroevolution, and many others. In these cases, science is being pushed by the evidence into finding what creationists have been predicting all along.

These illustrate to me that I am correct in thinking that the biblical worldview is the correct one. The Bible doesn't tell us about proteins or epigenetics or rock formations, but what it does is open our minds to a more correct way of viewing the world and its history. When our minds are thus *opened* we see things that others see as puzzling oddities—we see them in a correct perspective, a perspective that allows us to find more satisfactory explanations of biology and geology. After our minds are opened to ask better *questions* and make better *predictions*, we can then use standard scientific procedures to find solid *answers* to those questions.

Rather than being a hindrance to science, the careful pursuit of this approach can be a huge asset to science. It will be more successful in the long run. Our faith in God and His Bible is the foundation of this thinking, and we find that our faith is rewarded as it leads to new discoveries in science.

That doesn't mean we have the answers to all our questions. Trust is not just in information, but real trust is based on a relationship with a person we have confidence in. To us as Christians, our trust is in Jesus Christ, who not only has seen all of earth history but died to give us life. He is a God worthy of our trust, even if we don't understand it all.

I don't expect that I have convinced you of all this, but I hope you will think about it. If you understand what I am saying you will at least understand Bible-believing scientists a lot better.

ED. I guess I do understand you better, and what I see is perplexing. You really do think that your understanding is more correct than that of most of the scientific community? Your imaginary God gives you a more accurate scientific perspective? I guess in a hundred years, maybe less, we will know whether your viewpoint or mine leads to more solid science. Meanwhile, I will be putting my influence on the side of the success of conventional science.

CARL. When you meet the Creator face-to-face, what will you say to Him? Richard Dawkins had some uncomfortable things to say about Him!

ED. There will never be such a meeting, of course, but if it did happen there are some things I would say! I will mention only one item, the most damning one for your God. He proposes to send those who reject Him to hell, where they will burn forever! Where can you find even the tiniest bit of loving morality or ethics in that?

CARL. That is a very big issue and has been for hundreds, even thousands, of years. I completely understand why this has driven many to become atheists, especially thoughtful people who ask the tough ethical questions. But again I suggest asking "what if." What if we have seriously misinterpreted the Bible on this topic? The Bible describes death as a sleep. The idea of eternal torment came not from the Bible but from various philosophers. Their ideas for eternal hellfire came from nonbiblical sources and involved some poor translations of key words. Then their ideas were introduced into Christianity in the first few centuries after Christ, especially in the fourth and fifth centuries.

ED. Another interesting issue to ponder. If you are right, why do so many Christians not see it that way? Eternal hellfire has been a standard Christian doctrine for many centuries.

CARL. Isn't it possible that some ideas, even ideas about God, have become so ingrained in our thinking over the centuries that it is difficult to think we may all have misunderstood?

ED. Creative thinking! Your point would be more convincing if more Christians understood it that way. I have just one last question—if your God really does have so much power, why does He not prevent all the killing?

CARL. Remember that early in our conversation I said that God values our freedom of choice. He will not *force* us to live the way He asks us to live. There can be no love without freedom. Freedom also brings danger—danger that some will make the wrong choices and make life miserable for others. In spite of that, God can accept our allegiance only if it comes by our choice, not by His coercion. He has also told us that the rebellion we see on earth will finally have to end. Then we all receive the results of *our choice*.

ED. Sometimes I wish you could be right. But don't think that you will baptize me tomorrow! You still have to deal with the science, and it's your biggest problem. Don't you see that?

CARL. I'm sorry that you think in those terms, but we each have the right to make our own choices. In one of our earlier conversations the idea came up that science doesn't deal with absolute truth. Science can only show us which of our theories best fits the evidence *available now*. I love science, seeking to discover something worthwhile, but I also value truth. I see the Bible as the best source of truth, even the best source for understanding geology. I can see that as the scientific search has progressed, it has found more and more evidence that agrees with the biblical concept of earth history, as long as we don't hold on to assumptions that keep us from seeing what is being discovered right in front of us.

ED. I can't get away from the thought that you are letting your own assumptions influence your scientific work. It seems that you and your friends who think as you do believe you have an inside track on truth and have to prove your odd worldview. Correct?

CARL. My friends and I don't worry whether we can prove our worldview or our interpretation of geological history. We have confidence that revelation has given a trustworthy understanding of that history, and it is not up to us to prove that. Actually, that confidence in Scripture gives us a sense of liberating freedom, since it is not up to us to prove anything. If we take an honest approach to research, truth will defend itself. We just seek to be honest with the evidence and open to new insights that our study can bring us to.

ED. Do you really think God tells you what is true? Your description of your approach seems like a lofty goal, but how can a human live up to such a goal of free-thinking objectivity?

CARL. We cannot reach that goal, in ourselves, without divine guidance. I don't know how that works. I have never heard God speaking any words in my ear. We don't have access to any private information that is not available to anyone else. I guess it is just that our openness to new ideas, with awareness of both the biblical worldview and the conventional thinking in our fields, causes us to notice things that we would otherwise not notice. We don't always get it all correct, but we have confidence that a biblical worldview will ultimately lead us in the right direction.

ED. You are getting right back into the old God-of-the-gaps mistake so common a century or two ago, especially in your biology explanations. I thought we had left that behind! When there was a gap in our scientific knowledge, like our inability to explain how life began, then God was called in to fill that gap—to create life.

CARL. That is a favorite criticism against those who believe in God, but actually modern science has turned the logic behind the God-of-the-gaps idea right on its head. Today, those who believe in the actions of God in origins don't do so to fill a gap in our knowledge—it is the other way around. The more we learn about the biochemistry of life, the more obvious it is that the beginning of life and the origin of so many different classes and phyla of organisms is impossible to explain without a creator. It is the *increase of knowledge*, not the lack of knowledge, that is driving us closer to the Creator. Belief in a God who created life and who initiated a global flood is still an assumption accepted by faith in the Bible message. Modern science keeps finding things that support that faith, however, making it even more believable.

ED. Well, I appreciate your candor, but I have the faith to think the opposite. You have faith in your God and His old book. I have the faith to think that all those knowledgeable conventional scientists will find the correct answers. I guess I am willing to leave that as the conclusion of our discussion.

CARL. Fair enough! That is an honest and insightful conclusion. I couldn't have stated it better myself. I have greatly appreciated your willingness to share these conversations and to seek to understand another's perspective.

Here we are, back home. Now don't forget that the shovel is yours. You can keep the extra crackers and cheese. Tell your family hello, and I hope to see you at the next Geological Society of America annual meeting.

Fiddler on the Roof

In the story *Fiddler on the Roof*, traditions are what bring stability to the Jewish community living in difficult times. Tevye, the father in the family of the story, values these traditions, but choices made by his three daughters bring increasing challenges to his traditions. At the first two marriages Tevye struggles to accept their choices, but he bends to accommodate his daughters' wishes. The third daughter pushes further; she chooses to marry a young Russian Gentile lad, and this brings Tevye to a crucial choice. He wavers but cannot accept her decision, because "if I bend that far I will break." In the end Tevye chooses to lose his daughter rather than vary from tradition and its accompanying cultural stability.

Over time, in the study of origins, science settled on the Darwinian tradition—all life is the result of chance mutations and natural selection through deep time. This firm commitment to a common tradition has brought a type of stability into science. Those who accept the tradition understand one another and work together toward a common objective. Those who doubt the tradition have increasingly come to be seen as outside the system. Challenging or questioning the basics of the tradition is not allowed, as it would threaten the Darwinian stability.

Tevye had to choose between tradition and his daughter, but in the end he may have realized that such a choice did not bring a good result. The story leaves the final outcome to our imagination.

In science, new evidence and independent thinkers are destabilizing the comfortable Darwinian tradition. The Darwinian Tevyes among us insist there is no problem—random mutations, natural selection, and deep time can answer all uncertainties. Can they really? Or was the stability just a facade, a false stability resulting from choices to allow only unquestioning faithfulness to one tradition, the Darwinian, naturalistic tradition?

The other option can also be seen as a tradition—the choice to go, to one extent or another, against the strict Darwinian tradition and question all or part of that tradition and allow the possibility that there may be an intelligent designer somewhere in the shadows.

Both cannot be true. Firmly held traditions may seem to bring stability, but they can't prevent individual freedom of thought and choice. The final outcome of this challenge is open for each of us to choose.

Recommended Reading

For further reading, begin with any recent textbook on physical geology or earth science. The list below is a partial bibliography of mostly secondary sources, which contain a large number of more primary sources for those who wish to dig deeper in the literature on faith and science.

For a good scholarly treatment of the topic of hellfire, see E. W. Fudge, *The Fire That Consumes: A Biblical and Historical Study of the Doctrine of Final Punishment* (New York: Open Road Distribution, 2001). E. W. Fudge is an evangelical theologian, and *Christianity Today* has called this book the standard work on the topic. See also E. W. Fudge, *Hell: A Final Word: The Surprising Truths I Found in the Bible* (Abilene, TX: Leafwood Publishers, 2012), a popular summary of Fudge's earlier scholarly book.

Ager, D. V. *The Nature of the Stratigraphical Record*. New York: John Wiley, 1993.

Axe, D. *Undeniable: How Biology Confirms Our Intuition That Life Is Designed*. New York: HarperCollins, 2016.

Behe, M. J. *Darwin's Black Box: The Biochemical Challenge to Evolution*. New York: Free Press, 1996.

———. "Self-Organization and Irreducibly Complex Systems: A Reply to Shanks and Joplin." *Philosophy of Science* 67, no. 1 (2000): 155–162.

———. *The Edge of Evolution: The Search for the Limits of Darwinism*. New York: Free Press, 2007.

Brand, L., and A. V. Chadwick. *Faith, Reason, and Earth History*. 3rd ed. Berrien Springs, MI: Andrews University Press, 2016.

Brand, L., and R. Davidson. *Choose You This Day: Why It Matters What You Believe About Creation*. Nampa, ID: Pacific Press, 2013.

Cabej, N. R. *Epigenetic Principles of Evolution*. London: Elsevier, 2012.

Chamberlin, T. C. "The Method of Multiple Working Hypotheses." *Science* 148, no. 3671 (1965): 754–759. This is a reprint of an earlier paper; see also *Journal of Geology* 103, no. 3 (1995): 349–354 for a reprint of the article with an introduction by D. C. Raup.

Coyne, J. A. *Why Evolution Is True*. New York: Viking, 2009.

———. *Faith Versus Fact: Why Science and Religion Are Incompatible*. New York: Penguin, 2015.

Dalrymple, G. B. *The Age of the Earth*. Stanford, CA: Stanford University Press, 1991.

Dembski, W. A. *Intelligent Design: The Bridge Between Science and Theology*. Downers Grove, IL: InterVarsity Press, 1999.

———, ed. *Mere Creation: Science, Faith and Intelligent Design*. Downers Grove, IL: InterVarsity Press, 1998.

Dennett, D. C. and A. Plantinga. *Science and Religion: Are They Compatible?* New York: Oxford University Press, 2011.

Denton, M. *Evolution: A Theory in Crisis*. Chevy Chase, MD: Adler and Adler, 1985.

———. *Evolution: Still a Theory in Crisis*. Seattle: Seattle: Discovery Institute, 2016.

de Queiroz, A. *The Monkey's Voyage: How Improbable Journeys Shaped the History of Life*. New York: Basic Books, 2014.

Faure, G., and T. M. Mensing. *Isotopes: Principles and Applications*. 3rd ed. Hoboken, NJ: John Wiley, 2005.

Francis, R. C. *Epigenetics: The Ultimate Mystery of Inheritance*. New York: W. W. Norton, 2011.

Futuyma, D. J. *Evolution*. 3rd ed. Sunderland, MA: Sinauer Associates, 2013.

Recommended Reading

Hughes, V. "Epigenetics: The Sins of the Father." *Nature* 507, no. 7490 (2014): 22–24.

Kuhn, T. S. *The Structure of Scientific Revolutions.* 2nd ed. Chicago: University of Chicago Press, 1957, 1970.

Losos, J. B. "What Darwin Got Wrong." *The Chronicle of Higher Education* (January 24, 2014): B13–B15. https://lososlab.oeb.harvard.edu/files/lososlab /files/chronicle_of_higher_ed._2014.pdf.

Marks, R. J. II, M. J. Behe, W. A. Dembski, B. L. Gordon, and J. C. Sanford, eds. *Biological Information: New Perspectives.* Tuck Link, Singapore: World Scientific Publishing, 2013.

Meyer, S. C. *Darwin's Doubt.* New York: HarperCollins, 2013.

Meyer, S. C. *Signature in the Cell.* New York: HarperOne, 2009.

Meyer, S. C., S. Minnich, J. Moneymaker, P. A. Nelson, and R. Seelke. *Explore Evolution: The Arguments for and Against Neo-Darwinism.* Melbourne: Hill House, 2007.

Moreland, J. P., S. C. Meyer, C. Shaw, A. K. Gauger, and W. Grudem, eds. *Theistic Evolution: A Scientific, Philosophical, and Theological Critique.* Wheaton, IL: Crossway, 2017.

Nagel, T. *Mind and Cosmos: Why the Materialist Neo-Darwinian Conception of Nature Is Almost Certainly False.* New York: Oxford University Press, 2012.

Numbers, R. *The Creationists.* New York: A. A. Knopf, 1992.

Pigliucci, M., and G. B. Müller, eds. *Evolution: The Extended Synthesis.* Cambridge, MA: MIT Press, 2010.

Plantinga, A. "Methodological Naturalism?" *Origins and Design* 18, no. 1 (1997).

Ratzsch, D. *Science and Its Limits: The Natural Sciences in Christian Perspective.* Downers Grove, IL: InterVarsity, 2000.

Sadler, P. M. "Sediment Accumulation Rates and the Completeness of Stratigraphic Sections." *Journal of Geology* 89, no. 5 (1981): 569–584.

Shapiro, J. A. *Evolution: A View From the 21st Century.* Upper Saddle River, NJ: FT Press Science, 2011.

Soennichsen, J. *Bretz's Flood: The Remarkable Story of a Rebel Geologist and the World's Greatest Flood.* Seattle: Sasquatch Books, 2008.

Strobel, L. *The Case for a Creator: A Journalist Investigates Scientific Evidence That Points Toward God.* Grand Rapids, MI: Zondervan 2004.

van Andel, T. H. "Consider the Incompleteness of the Geological Record." *Nature* 294 (1981): 397–398.

Woodward, T. E., and J. P. Gills. *The Mysterious Epigenome: What Lies Beyond DNA.* Grand Rapids, MI: Kregel, 2012.

Glossary

In order to make this book accessible to a wide range of readers, this glossary defines a set of terms and concepts that may not be familiar to someone without a background in evolutionary biology, geology, or the Bible.

abiogenesis—The theory that the first living cells on earth developed from nonliving material by natural processes over millions of years; no creation or intelligent design of life.

assumption—Something that is believed without being based on any direct evidence. For example, many persons believe life came into being with no creation or intelligent design, but this a belief (assumption) not based on any evidence; it is based on a philosophy.

Cambrian explosion—The event at the beginning of the Cambrian in which virtually all of the phyla of animals that are found as fossils appear in the fossil record at essentially the same time. At other levels in the fossil record, specific groups (e.g., orders or families) of fossils appear almost all at once (other explosions). For example, most of the orders of mammals first appear at or near the beginning of the Eocene.

chemical evolution—See abiogenesis.

continental drift—The theory that continents have moved around on the earth over the course of geological history. The theory that explains these movements is called plate tectonics.

conventional science—The type of scientific thinking and practice that accepts deep time and evolution of life over millions of years and believes that processes through geological history were the same as processes observable today, or that are feasible on the earth today. The majority approach to science (sometimes also called standard science).

creation—In this book, creation means the bringing into existence of life or of any group of organisms by God, the Intelligent Designer who calls these organisms into existence instantaneously.

creationist—In this book, the term is used to refer to a person who accepts a set of concepts, including (1) the origin of life and of the major life-forms or body plans by creation in a week of time, a few thousand years ago; and (2) the biblical account that some centuries later a catastrophic global flood restructured the earth's crust and killed most animals and humans (these are described in the biblical book of Genesis). The Flood occurred because the human race had sinned and rebelled and become so corrupt and violent from the influence of Satan (a literal powerful angel who rebelled against God) that Satan almost had the entire race under his control; only a few responded to God's warnings and sought the refuge from the Flood that God provided. This same biblical belief includes the Satan-instigated death of Jesus, the Son of God, and His resurrection, to win back those humans who accept His sacrifice for them. Many persons who accept this scenario are Christians.

Darwinism—The evolutionary theory claiming that all life-forms evolved from common ancestors by a series of biological changes resulting from random mutations to their DNA. Individuals with the best set of new characteristics are more likely to live and reproduce because of natural selection.

deep time—The concept that life has been on earth for at least hundreds of millions of years, rather than thousands of years.

eolian—A name for the process of depositing sediment by wind, such as forming sand dunes in a desert. The other (and by far the most common) geological process for depositing sediment is by flowing water.

epigenetics—A fairly new concept in the field of genetics, which recognizes that many biological changes are the result of a management system outside of or above the genes in DNA. Epigenetic processes turn genes on or off, or modify their effects. These changes do not involve mutations; they do not change the DNA but manage how the information in DNA is used by the organism.

evolution—See Darwinism; most evolutionists think evolution occurs by the process defined there.

faith—A belief that goes beyond the direct evidence that we have. For example, faith that life was created, or faith that life was not created.

fossil record—The series of fossil organisms in the geological column, from Precambrian to Recent. Animal fossils are only from Cambrian to Recent. See the figure on page 9.

geological column—The stack of rock layers covering the earth. See the figure on page 9.

geology—The study of rocks and of how sediments like sand, mud, or pebbles are deposited and cemented to form, respectively, sandstone, mudstone or shale, or conglomerate (sand plus pebbles or larger particles). Geologists also seek to understand other topics, including the processes that uplift and erode rocks to form our existing landscape.

macroevolution—In this book, it is used to refer to origin by evolution of major groups of organisms; origin of new orders, classes, and phyla (a phylum is generally equivalent to a body plan; [e.g., flatworm, clam, insect, or vertebrate body plan]). Macroevolution involves evolution of new body plans, new organs and body parts, and many new genes. A debate is ongoing over whether macroevolution results from the accumulation of many episodes of microevolution or whether macroevolution occurs through a different process than microevolution.

methodological naturalism (MN)—A version of naturalism (see page 96) that does not address whether there is a God. It is only a method of science, which does not allow any supernatural explanations to be used in scientific explanations. In some ways it is harmless, but in practice it is often dogmatically applied even to explanations of events in the ancient past, like the origin of life, and to deep time and ancient geological events that we can't observe; thus, it is something we should not be dogmatic about.

microevolution—Biological changes within a species of animal or plant. This same process also makes the changes that can result in a new genus. This process is compatible with creationist thinking as well as with Darwinian evolution theory. Microevolution involves small changes not resulting in new organs, new anatomical structures, and probably no new genes.

natural selection—Increased likelihood of survival and reproduction of individuals who are better adapted to their environment. For example, mammals or birds that are white in winter to match the snow in their habitat will be less likely to be seen by predators.

naturalism—The philosophy that seeks to explain all events and processes in history by the actions of the laws of chemistry and physics. Does not allow any divine or supernatural explanations to be used in science.

orphan genes—Or ORFan genes; genes that appear in a type of organism with no ancestor genes in other organisms from which the orphan gene could have evolved. Orphan genes were discovered when it became possible to sequence the genomes of organisms.

phylogenetic tree—A tree-shaped diagram showing the presumed evolutionary history of a group of animals or plants.

radiometric dating—Establishing a date for a rock layer (generally a volcanic layer) using an isotope of an element that is unstable and decays through time into a different isotope. If the rate of decay is known and the proportion of the isotope that has changed (decayed) is known, an age for the sample can be calculated, with application of some assumptions.

speciation—The division of a population of organisms into two groups that do not interbreed, making them different species.

unconformity—A level in the geological column where some disturbance appears between one sediment layer and the next layer. There may be evidence of erosion between those two layers, or evidence that after the lower layer was in place, significant time passed before the upper layer was deposited.

worldview—Any philosophy that provides answers to the big questions of life, like where we came from, why we are here, and where (if anywhere) we are going. Such a philosophy also influences many smaller aspects of life: how we think about what is happening around us and what things we notice. For example, Christianity and naturalistic evolution theory are worldviews.